Free To Choose Medicine

How Faster Access to New Drugs
Would Save Countless Lives and
End Needless Suffering

Bartley J. Madden

Free To Choose Medicine

Published by The Heartland Institute
19 South LaSalle Street #903
Chicago, Illinois 60603
phone 312/377-4000
fax 312/377-5000
www.heartland.org

Additional copies of this book
are available from The Heartland Institute
for the following prices:

1-10 copies	$8.95 per copy
11-50 copies	$7.95 per copy
51-100 copies	$6.95 per copy
101 or more	$5.95 per copy

Printed in the United States of America
ISBN-13 978-1-934791-32-5
ISBN-10 1-934791-32-6

Manufactured in the United States of America

Contents

Praise for
Free To Choose Medicine

Bart Madden brings to his task a thorough knowledge of the issues that must be confronted and a deep concern for improving the rules that govern FDA processes. It's about defining an FDA track that empowers the patients and physicians who have the relevant knowledge and need the freedom to choose to use that knowledge without harming others. This is a book that can be studied fruitfully by all who have a concern for these problems. It is fundamentally bipartisan and should be read in that spirit.

Vernon L. Smith
Economic Science Institute, Chapman University
Nobel Laureate in Economics, 2002

Free To Choose Medicine is full of disturbing data about the unintended consequences of our nation's quest for safe drugs seemingly without regard to cost. Bart Madden explains how we have lost sight of the goals of encouraging innovation, speed to market, and quick access for suffering patients, and he lays out a realistic plan for getting back on track.

Hon. Jim DeMint
U.S. Senator - South Carolina

A provocative proposal that offers a libertarian solution for reform of the nation's dysfunctional drug regulation.

Henry I. Miller, M.D.
Former Director of the FDA's Office of Biotechnology
Research Fellow, Hoover Institution

Many take for granted that government regulation is necessary to protect us from unsafe and ineffective drugs. Bart Madden's important new book challenges that conventional wisdom and stands it on its head. He shows that it is we who need protection from a dangerous regulatory system that keeps too many innovative drugs off the market for too long. He also shows how greater freedom for patients and doctors can lead us out of this counterproductive regulatory process. Everyone with an interest in health policy should read this book. It deals forcefully with an issue that is, quite literally, a matter of life or death.

Sam Peltzman
Ralph and Dorothy Keller Distinguished Service Professor
Emeritus of Economics
University of Chicago

Bart Madden shines a bright light on the all-too-invisible damage caused by the FDA's self-protective, dysfunctional, and ultimately lethal drug approval process. He explains how the FDA bureaucracy protects itself while allowing millions of people to suffer and die who could be helped by faster access to the newest medicines. The FDA uses approval processes appropriate to an era of adding machines and not super computers. Madden offers a 21st century information-age solution in *Free To Choose Medicine* that would give consumers control over health decisions, allow faster access to life-saving and life-enhancing drugs, and ultimately reduce the cost of new medicines. This concise book explains how to keep the FDA monopoly from stifling innovation and crippling the life sciences industry. Madden offers the right cure for the ailing FDA.

Grace-Marie Turner
President
Galen Institute

Madden's book is an excellent summary of the arguments many of us have made to suggest the need for change in the hidebound FDA regulated, drug development system. Dual Tracking and Freedom to Choose are specific proposals of real interest. Unfortunately, in addressing the problems in our drug development system for over 25 years, I have seen no credible evidence that the FDA has any interest in substantial change. The FDA responds (if they do at all) to critics with lip service, obfuscation or intimidation. I hope Bart Madden's book will elicit a real response and debate leading to substantial change that will benefit patients.

Robert K. Oldham, M.D.
Cancer Cellular Therapeutics, Inc.

As the President promotes his plan to increase the role of government in our health care, this timely and topical book brings some very important new ideas to the debate. By allowing individuals to contract with drug developers so they can gain access to innovative drugs that have completed safety trials, Americans will have the opportunity to live longer and healthier lives. The cost of new drugs will decline and research and development into new treatments will increase. It is a must-read for all legislators and the general public.

Sally C. Pipes
President
Pacific Research Institute

Foreword

It is my pleasure to endorse Bart Madden's thoughtful call for careful reevaluation of the Food and Drug Administration process of drug approval.

The issue is not, nor should it be, that there is no role for standards of quality and testing, but that such processes must not interfere arbitrarily with what are properly and legitimately decisions between physicians and patients based on individual circumstances.

There are two kinds of error when considering the harm that any drug testing-approval process can cause. There is the error of approving a drug that may have safety and efficacy risks, and the error of failing to approve in a timely manner a drug that can prevent deaths already occurring. The balancing of these two errors is politically difficult for the FDA. Why? Because any drug that gets through the FDA screen and causes injury or death is likely to cause widespread negative publicity for the agency and calls for tightening the FDA's already too-fine screen or otherwise "doing something" to prevent reoccurrence.

Alternatively, any drug that is delayed for a year or two or longer and would have been efficacious will fail to prevent injury or death for those who are not treated – silent private events that are not newsworthy, but in aggregate cause large amounts of unnecessary suffering and deaths. This tradeoff is inherent in the uncertainties of medical treatment and the advance of knowledge. It is not due to evil people. Everybody involved can be doing his or her job faithfully according to the rules, but those rules are failing to correct a growing imbalance between the damages caused by these two types of error.

Bart Madden carefully develops the fundamental reasons for breaking the FDA's monopoly on access to drugs. One stake in the ground is the common-sense principle that patients and their doctors should control medical treatment, including access to not-yet-FDA-approved drugs.

Using sound economic principles, he argues that the FDA's one-size-fits-all regulatory scheme is flawed. It does not allow individuals to express their preferences for risk versus potential health improvement. Moreover, there is no feedback mechanism to evaluate the benefits versus costs of the hugely expensive and lengthy FDA clinical trials. The negative consequences to society of failing to modify this regulatory process will worsen as the pace of medical innovation accelerates. Hence, the importance of modernizing overdue reforms in FDA procedures.

Madden's market-based solution appeals to economists like me who are keenly aware of the critical importance of institutional design for a system to promote decentralized responses close to the local knowledge that is available to physicians and their patients, but not to the FDA.

The first component of Madden's plan is a "Dual Tracking" arrangement. On one track, a new drug continues along the conventional FDA clinical-testing procedures. On a separate track, independent of the FDA, new drugs that have passed Phase I safety trials can be bought by informed consumers (patients with advice from their doctors) by legally contracting with drug developers. Patients and their doctors could choose either FDA-approved drugs or new drugs still in clinical trials.

The second component is a Tradeoff Evaluation Database (TED) that allows convenient access to the information patients and doctors need to be adequately informed about the risks of adverse side effects and potential health improvements. TED also incorporates the private sector in a way that promotes informed choice among alternatives throughout the system.

These design components for patient/doctor control of medical treatment are both innovative and soundly based. With Madden's conceptual blueprint, legislation could be crafted to promote both expanded consumer choice and the discipline of choice to the long-term benefit of society.

Bart Madden brings to his task a thorough knowledge of the issues that must be confronted and a deep concern for improving the rules that govern FDA processes. It's about defining an FDA track that empowers the patients and physicians who have the relevant knowledge and need the freedom to choose to use that knowledge without harming others. This is a document that can be studied fruitfully by all who have a concern for these problems. It is fundamentally bipartisan and should be read in that spirit.

Vernon L. Smith
Economic Science Institute, Chapman University
2002 Nobel Laureate in Economics

Preface

FDA reform became a top priority for me after reading the tragic details of how cancer patients were dying without access to the promising new drugs being tested in clinical trials and therefore not available in the marketplace. This struck me as an enormously important problem crying out for a solution. My approach to a workable solution for this problem comes from my research work.

My career mostly involved learning how markets work and applying a systems mindset to problems in general, and economic problems in particular. Some of this research is summarized in my book *Wealth Creation: A Systems Mindset for Building and Investing in Businesses for the Long Term* (John Wiley & Sons, Inc., 2010). Wealth creation is rooted in individuals making decisions in their own best interests. That same principle applies to better health through FDA reform.

My two main ideas about FDA reform are:

(1) The FDA itself is the bottleneck in the drugs-to-patients system, the goal of which is better drugs, sooner, at lower cost. As a practical matter, the FDA's continual push for more extensive clinical testing ignores the importance of providing new drugs sooner, at lower cost.

(2) The system solution is to introduce consumer choice. Patients could then decide whether to use not-yet-approved new drugs based on their unique health condition and risk preference.

I wrote a series of articles in journals, magazines, and newspapers that laid out the practical details of what I now call Free To Choose Medicine. One of my articles was packaged as a booklet, *More Choices, Better Health: Free to Choose Experimental Drugs* published by The Heartland Institute and translated into several foreign languages. That led to productive dialogues, both at home and abroad, with pharmaceutical industry and academic experts who agreed and disagreed with my views. Eventually, I was satisfied that all the important issues had been covered and it was time for a short, informative book.

The goal for this book is to give you an easy-to-read, condensed, yet comprehensive case for the freedom to use drugs that are only part way through the long FDA approval process. After reading this book, you will have a working knowledge of the FDA drug approval process, a clear understanding of the enormous benefits a Free To Choose Medicine Act would bring, and the ability to see through the false arguments of those who want ever-more-stringent FDA testing that, in reality, amounts to deadly overcaution. My hope is that you will then become an enthusiastic supporter of a reform movement to enact legislation that enables patients, advised by their doctors, to make informed decisions about the use of not-yet-FDA-approved therapeutic drugs.

Why support the Free To Choose Medicine proposal and not some other plan? Two reasons. First, in my opinion, the proposal in this book addresses the many practical design details necessary to optimize the benefits of consumer choice and overcome anticipated lobbying efforts by trial lawyers to kill freedom of choice legislation before it sees the light of day. As explained in Chapter 4, such freedom requires that users of not-yet-approved drugs take personal responsibility for any adverse outcomes in a manner that minimizes the opportunities for the frivolous lawsuits that are all too common in the medical malpractice area.

Second, Free To Choose Medicine offers a way around the FDA regulatory process by being independent of its bureaucracy. That is a unique benefit missing from the typical FDA reform plan. Consequently, a Free To Choose Medicine Act, once implemented, almost certainly could not be neutralized later by the FDA because the agency would not be in charge of it. Nor could government easily dilute what citizens would come to view as their right to freedom of choice.

Free To Choose Medicine builds upon the extraordinary work of many scholars and patient activists whose family members were lost without having an opportunity to use the drugs that they and their doctors believed would have been in their best interest. I have benefited from the insightful articles and books written by the individuals mentioned below. Excerpts from their work are quoted and/or referenced in the chapters that follow.

Daniel Klein and Alex Tabarrok at George Mason University created www.FDAReview.org, which is a uniquely valuable source for understanding FDA issues. Over the years, Alex has provided very useful critiques of my FDA work, including this book.

At the University of Chicago: Sam Peltzman is a pioneer in showing that the 1962 legislation that required clinical trials to test drug efficacy did not yield benefits to society in excess of the costs involved. Gary Becker makes the case for freedom of choice implemented using the Internet as a way for patients to make informed decisions. Richard Epstein has produced devastating critiques of the FDA monopoly, while educating us about the legal issues involved.

At the Competitive Enterprise Institute: Sam Kazman heads up CEI's Death By Regulation project. Greg Conko provides astute analyses of many issues in food and drug safety regulation. Greg's especially detailed comments on this book definitely helped to improve the final product.

At the American Enterprise Institute: Scott Gottlieb, a doctor and former high-ranking FDA official, is particularly strong in dissecting how government bureaucracy creates health care inefficiencies. John Calfee provides sound economic analyses ranging from FDA and pharmaceutical industry issues to liability and consumer information concerns.

At the Hoover Institution, Henry Miller has wide-ranging experience working in FDA management and is noted for his skill in analyzing and communicating complex medical issues. And Robert Higgs at the Independent Institute brings a hard-core libertarian perspective to FDA analysis. He wrote a classic article showing how consumers are worse off due to the FDA's monopoly on access to new drugs.

Steve Walker, co-founder of the Abigail Alliance for Better Access to Developmental Drugs, lost his wife to cancer and became intimately familiar with the deeply rooted problems created by the FDA's monopoly on drugs. Few people are as passionate and knowledgeable about the need for FDA reform as Steve.

In the past few years, Alphonse Crespo, Susan Dudley, James Gubb, Sheridan Lam, and Scott Riccio have sharpened my thinking in many ways. Marie Murray has skillfully edited all of my FDA work, including this book, and improved both the presentation and the content. Ernie Welker has a special talent for improving economic arguments and his work on this book is appreciated. Joseph Bast, president of The Heartland Institute, contributed many ideas, including the section "What You Can Do Right Now." I especially appreciate the skilled, editorial fine-tuning contributed by Diane Bast and the creative design of the cover and figures by Kevin Fitzgerald.

Chapter 1
Sacrificing Patients
to the FDA

I concluded that the [FDA] proof-of-efficacy requirement was a public health disaster, promoting much more sickness and death than it prevented. Nothing I have seen since has moved me to change that conclusion – the disaster is ongoing.

Sam Peltzman
Regulation and the Natural Progress of Opulence, 2005

This book makes the case that we need to be free to make informed decisions about whether to use not-yet-FDA-approved therapeutic drugs – that is, new drugs that have successfully passed safety trials, generated preliminary efficacy data, and may offer us the opportunity to improve our health or even save our life. The following brief stories reveal the importance of this issue for you, your family, and all Americans.

Abigail Burroughs
Frank Burroughs' only child, Abigail, was stricken with neck cancer and died at the age of 21. For such a young person, she displayed remarkable compassion with a spirit focused on living her life to the highest standards. At her high school graduation ceremony, Abigail spoke these words, "Success is fleeting, but when all is said and done, all you have is your character."

There was hope for Abigail in the form of a promising drug, Erbitux, that her highly respected oncologist believed could help her. Erbitux was a new drug being tested in clinical trials. But Abigail could not enroll in a clinical trial because her cancer was not in a part of her body that the trial required. Erbitux was later approved – too late for Abigail.

A week and a half before she died, Abigail did an extensive television interview as part of an effort by herself and her father to educate people about the life and death consequences of the lack of patient access to promising new drugs. During the interview, Abigail told the audience, "This is not just about me. This is about so many others."

Frank then decided to devote his life to helping people who confront life-threatening diseases with time running out. He co-founded the Abigail Alliance for Better Access to Developmental Drugs – an organization that helps people gain access to promising therapeutic drugs slowly making their way through the FDA's clinical trial process. A picture of Abigail that captures her spirit in a memorable way is posted on the first page of the Abigail Alliance website, http://www.abigail-alliance.org.

Kianna Karnes

Kianna Karnes experienced first-hand the difficulties in obtaining especially promising, new, and not-yet-approved drugs that had the potential to save her life. She was the mother of four children and died at the age of 44 from kidney cancer.

Normally this would have been just another invisible case of freedom of choice denied. But *The Wall Street Journal* ran an editorial, "Kianna's Law," that urged politicians to pass a law enabling patients with life-threatening diseases to avoid the often-futile attempt to secure "compassionate use" from the FDA and the risk of getting a placebo in a clinical trial. Instead, patients and their doctors would be able to directly access a promising new drug.

Under the glare of national publicity, the FDA approved Kianna's request. But the agency's approval arrived the day she died.

Kianna's father, John Rowe, had earlier experience with clinical trials. He was diagnosed with leukemia and was fortunate not only to be accepted in a clinical trial for Gleevec, a revolutionary new drug for treating leukemia, but also to actually receive Gleevec. The comparison drug, interferon, already known to be of only marginal effectiveness, was also being randomly administered as part of a comparison in the clinical trial. As of this writing, Gleevec has kept his cancer in remission.

John Rowe's words about losing his daughter are more than enough reason for me to have written this book and for you to read it:

Here is a case where her old man understood clinical trials. I knew about compassionate use; I had a friendship with a powerful member of Congress; I've got *The Wall Street Journal* behind me. But I still couldn't save her life. Now, what about the thousands of people out there who don't have these kinds of resources available to them? I don't know that either of these drugs would have saved Kianna's life. But wouldn't it have been nice to give her a chance?[1]

Multiple Sclerosis (MS) Patients

Any single death from the denial of access to a promising new drug is profoundly sad for the victim's family and loved ones. So too is the unnecessary pain and suffering of much larger numbers of victims who are denied access to drugs that could significantly better manage their diseases. Multiple sclerosis is but one example of that.

Multiple sclerosis, or MS, is a disease of the nervous system that can cause difficulty in maintaining balance when walking, a painful loss of eyesight, and an almost constant state of fatigue. At the present time, between 250,000 and 350,000 people in the United States have been diagnosed with MS.

An approved drug for treating MS, Tysabri, demonstrated in clinical trials a remarkable ability to decrease both "relapses" as well as the formation of additional brain lesions. But in 2005, following two deaths apparently caused by adverse effects from the drug, Tysabri was pulled from the market. Many MS patients immediately pleaded with the FDA to restore access to Tysabri and the FDA eventually agreed. Even so, while the drug was off the market, hundreds of thousands of people suffered.

John Calfee, an economist with the American Enterprise Institute, reported survey responses of MS patients who were asked if they were willing to take their chances with Tysabri, despite its apparent 1 in 1,000 chance of causing fatal complications.[2] Roughly half of the patients said they were willing to take the risk.

Additionally, 71 percent of the MS patients surveyed agreed with the following statements, "If a drug has safety concerns, the FDA should warn people, but I should be free to decide with my doctor whether to use those drugs or not" and "I am capable of making my own treatment choices, based on the information and advice I get from my doctor."

Prostate Cancer Activists

Dendreon, a biotech company, developed a strikingly innovative cancer vaccine (Provenge) that triggers the body's natural immune defenses to recognize cancer cells and kill them. Provenge is for men with prostate cancer, a disease that kills 30,000 men every year in the U.S. From Dendreon's founding in 1992 to the FDA's advisory panel meeting to recommend a course of action for Provenge, Dendreon had spent approximately $500 million of risk capital supplied by investors judging that the firm's science would be successfully commercialized.

In March 2007, the FDA advisory panel voted 17-0 that Provenge was safe and 13-4 that the drug demonstrated substantial evidence of efficacy. Given the advisory panel's vote, approval seemed highly likely and expectations were that a better treatment for prostate cancer would be available shortly. But the FDA denied approval, instead instructing Dendreon to complete another clinical trial that would most likely take two to three years. Two to three years of denied access would mean 60,000 to 90,000 men with prostate cancer would die without the choice to use an apparently safe and promising new treatment.

You might think the FDA would be reluctant to make decisions that have such a high cost, but it is not. For the presumed benefit of future patients, the FDA asserts that its testing process requires existing patients to forego any freedom of choice.

In this particular case, patients fought back. Men with advanced prostate cancer formed patient advocacy groups to call for immediate access to Provenge. One memorable advertisement by the advocacy groups was headlined "Dysfunction at the FDA: Prostate Cancer Victims Face Needless Suffering and Premature Death." But the FDA is accustomed to ignoring the voices of today's patients and, with the exception of the AIDS/HIV activists in the 1980s, this strategy has been successful for the FDA.

In April 2009, Dendreon announced that the results of its pivotal clinical trial exceeded the FDA's statistical milestones and validated the goal of harnessing a patient's own immune system to fight cancer. With these new, strong results, Dendreon was able to raise an additional $230 million of equity capital from investors. The next step is once again to seek FDA approval. During this time, more men with prostate cancer will die.

Whose Choice Is It?

The shared opinion of those 71 percent of surveyed MS patients that "I should be free to decide with my doctor whether to use those drugs or not" is the point of this book. These tragic stories and statistics are offered to begin to make the case that people should be free to choose the medicines they want, without having to wait for completion of government-mandated clinical trials and analyses that can take a decade or more.

Steve Walker gives us an idea of what it really means to be denied freedom of choice when your life is on the line.

> Consider the plight of such [terminally ill] patients. They search for clinical trials of new drugs that might extend their lives. Nearly all are ineligible. Of the few who do qualify, many learn the trial is fully enrolled and closed, or too far away. Others face a 50-50 chance of getting a placebo (a sugar pill) under blinded conditions (meaning neither they nor their doctors know what they are getting). Many are allowed to die without being told about or offered the active drug.[3]

On the face of it, this is an egregious injustice, an unnecessary loss of lives, even a crime against humanity.

"The issue, after all, is not whether the drug works or whether it sometimes kills people," writes John Calfee. "It is whether the tradeoff is worth it: Is a 1 in 1,000 chance of dying a risk worth running …? The experts on these questions are the patients. They are the only ones who can balance [their] quality-of-life against the risk of death. Their view should be absolutely paramount."[4]

Most people agree with Calfee. In a national survey conducted by the National Consumers League, 94 percent of respondents agreed with the statement, "All medications, both over-the-counter and prescription, offer benefits but also carry some risk of side effects. It should be up to physicians and patients to weigh the benefits against the risks and to make decisions that are right for them."[5]

The amount of risk patients are willing to accept for potential improvement to their health is not static. Health conditions change over time, pain can become intolerable, the degeneration associated with Parkinson's disease, MS, or Alzheimer's often becomes disabling, and for some there is little hope for survival using the drugs that have secured conventional FDA approval. Further, the amount of useful data about drugs grows over time, leading doctors and patients to change their opinions about how effective and how risky a new drug might be.

With today's system, the patient must meet the needs of the FDA's mandated clinical trial criteria – or, in almost all cases, get nothing. A single arbitrary level of risk is chosen by the FDA's risk-averse bureaucracy and imposed on everyone. Such a system cannot help but fail to achieve its stated objective of "advancing the public health by helping to speed innovations that make medicines and foods more effective, safer, and more affordable" (See "What We Do" at the FDA's website, www.fda.org.)

What Is Missing from the Health Care Debate?

As I am writing this book, the attention of the nation is riveted on the debate over how to restructure the country's health care system. You might think that getting better drugs to patients who need them, sooner and at lower cost, would be a major part of that debate. You would be wrong.

Much greater government control is said to be necessary, in part to "bend the curve" of health care costs downward. The rising cost of prescription drugs, reflecting both higher prices and increased use, is often cited as a major cause of accelerating health care costs in America. Proposals to fix the system often contain provisions that would have the government control prescription drug prices.

Missing from the debate is an understanding of the overall drugs-to-patients *system* and of the current government policies that needlessly delay access to drugs and greatly increase their cost. Also missing is sufficient appreciation for the lives extended and quality-of-life improvements made possible by innovative drugs and medical devices. To mention just one type of drug, the estimated monetary value to society of the HIV/AIDS therapies that were introduced beginning in the late 1980s is $1.4 trillion, according to a 2006 study.[6] Of that total, 95 percent represented health benefits to patients and only 5 percent accrued to private-sector drug developers. That seems to have been a remarkably good bargain for society.

In theory, public-sector organizations could develop breakthrough new drugs but, in practice, this has not happened. Only the profit-motivated private sector has consistently delivered the goods.[7] Between 1988 and 2000, life expectancy for cancer patients increased by approximately four years.[8] With Genetech's drug Lucentis, 95 percent of patients with wet macular degeneration experienced an end to their vision deterioration and 40 percent experienced improved vision.[9]

Concern over the cost of health care so dominates the attention of politicians and reform advocates that little attention is given to the role of innovation that yields highly effective drugs such as Lucentis. Ignored is the average billion-dollar cost drug companies incur to obtain FDA approval for a new drug. Also ignored is the possibility that changing the current drug approval process could substantially reduce the cost of new drugs.

Imposing price controls on drugs, rather than addressing the way patients get access to new drugs, may seem easier and faster – a more "direct route" to solving an apparent problem. It is not. Price controls strict enough to have a substantial impact on drug costs would decimate investment in new drug development because developers would be unable to earn an adequate return on their investors' capital. Investment capital would go elsewhere. Small biotech companies – the source of so many of the new drugs that are revolutionizing medicine – would become an endangered species.

Scott Gottlieb, a doctor who has held several positions with the FDA, warned in 2009:

> … [C]apital may well start shifting to other enterprises as the Obama administration unveils policies that diminish the incentives to invest in new medical products. There is precedent for the availability of this sort of capital to turn on a proverbial dime. Shortly after President Bill Clinton unveiled his proposal for nationalizing the health insurance market in the 1990s (with similar limits on access to medical care as in the Obama plan), biotech venture capital fell by more than a third in a single year, and the value of biotech stocks fell 40 percent. It took three years for the 'Biocentury' stock index to recover. Not surprisingly, many companies went out of business.[10]

More regulation is not going to get us better drugs, sooner, at lower cost. The real solution is simpler. It is to allow patients, with the advice of their doctors, to choose to use not-yet-approved drugs. Free To Choose Medicine would improve the health of millions of people and extend the lives of hundreds of thousands.

Why We Don't Already Have a Grassroots Movement

With so much unnecessary suffering and dying, why isn't there a grassroots movement for Free To Choose Medicine? I can give four reasons.

First, the nightly news keeps most of us frightened about serious adverse side effects (including death) from the use of approved drugs. We rarely see stories blaming deaths on unnecessary regulatory delay by the FDA, even though many thousands of such deaths occur for every one death due to an approved drug. Such biased presentations lead many people to believe that an even-stronger FDA is needed to perform even-more-stringent testing of drugs.

It is apparent that few reporters have viewed the discovery, testing, and sale of new drugs as a system that is failing because of the faulty design of one of its components. Or that suffering and deaths would be greatly reduced if promising new drugs moved faster through clinical testing. Reporters don't write about what they can't readily see.

Second, the FDA and its supporters erroneously believe they are serving the public interest. Actually, they are highly motivated to preserve their authority by defending the status quo. They maintain their power, in part, by banging the drum of fear that any weakening of FDA powers would unleash a torrent of harmful drugs on the public. So far, that has worked. Pharmaceutical company experts who could contradict this claim are often silent out of fear of antagonizing the regulators whose decisions can spell the difference between their company's financial success or failure.

Third, most of us have not realized, thought about, or been able to evaluate what economists call the "opportunity cost" of not being free to make an informed choice about the best drug treatment. It is a freedom we once had prior to legislation in 1962. That legislation granted the FDA, in effect, a monopoly over access to drugs, thus preventing people from expressing their preferences.

Finally, only a small percentage of people at any given time personally experience pain, suffering, and the prospect of death due to denied access to new drugs. Consequently, most of us, most of the time, do not have the passion to demand legislation to secure this freedom. If and when we ever do experience such pain or face such a prospect, our illness may consume so much of our energy and resources that joining a coalition or writing a letter to a congressman will appear very low on our "to-do list." FDA bureaucrats, on the other hand, devote their entire careers, along with millions of taxpayer dollars, to defending their faulty system.

Healthier, Longer, and More Productive Lives

Throughout this book, I'll stress a systems mindset that views the FDA as one component of the complex drugs-to-patients system. Absent a systems mindset, more extensive FDA clinical testing is automatically viewed as a good thing to do regardless of the negative consequences elsewhere in the system. A fundamental point is that the systems perspective provides the compelling argument that the FDA itself is the bottleneck in achieving the system's goal of better drugs, sooner, at lower cost.

Consumer choice and competition are the heart of a market system. They are especially relevant in achieving truly large-scale benefits from Free To Choose Medicine. This becomes apparent as we analyze how the FDA testing process works (Chapter 2), what supporters say in its defense (Chapter 3), and how we can fix it (Chapter 4).

Chapter 5 lays out the practical tasks to begin building a reform movement that, if this book does the job I hope it will, you would want to join. The basic reason is this: We all want healthier, longer, and more-productive lives for ourselves, our family members, and all Americans.

Chapter 2
Getting Drugs to Patients Is a System

Nothing in government corresponds to the market process of spontaneous
coordination of decentralized decisions; nothing corresponds to its way of
bringing even remote considerations to the attention of each decentralized
decision maker in the form of prices.

Leland B. Yeager
"Is There A Bias Toward Overregulation?" (1983)

In order to effectively analyze how new drugs make their way to patients,
one needs to understand "systems thinking," a few facts about how markets
function, the role of government in market systems, and the role played by
the FDA in the drugs-to-patients system. Proceeding in this logical way
makes it clear why the current FDA regulatory process is ill-suited to
achieving the goal of better drugs, sooner, at lower cost.

Systems Thinking
A system is composed of parts that work together to achieve a goal while
utilizing feedback to adapt to any disturbances in the system's environment.
We live in a networked world of systems interacting within systems.
Systems thinking entails awareness that complexity pervades relationships
among components within a system as well as the relationships among
systems.

To apply systems thinking, we need to be conscious of how we go
about *perceiving* what we take to be reality, *acting* to achieve the purpose
we choose, and *knowing* what the consequences of our actions are expected
to be.[1] This knowing process can be broken into six components:

1. Purpose. Purposes are the outcomes we, as individuals, seek from the actions we take. A systems mindset requires that we clearly state our purposes (goals), rather than proceed with purposes that are vague or contradictory.

2. Perceptions. Philosophers and scientists have long debated the relationship between what we perceive with our senses and what is "reality." Thinking that there is a pure, independent reality needs to be replaced with the concept that our individual "reality" is a function of our past experiences and current knowledge base. Our perceptions are *always* incomplete, and many bad decisions are made because we mistakenly assume they provide us with a sufficiently reliable picture of reality.

3. Cause and Effect. Oftentimes it is easy – too easy – to isolate a presumed cause of a problem in one component of a system. Although fixing this problem may improve *local efficiency*, it may not result in improved performance of the overall system.

4. Actions and Consequences. We analyze cause and effect in order to take actions that will yield desired consequences. Because every action is embedded in a system, which itself is part of another system, and so on, many actions will have *unintended consequences*. A systems mindset can help us to take actions that minimize adverse unintended consequences.

5. Feedback. A healthy skepticism of our knowledge base leads us to embrace experimentation in order to discover obsolete assumptions and test new ideas. Experimentation to get feedback information can easily be seen in the work of designers. They build prototypes to expedite their learning as to how to translate a client-specified goal into a functioning product.

6. Knowledge Base. Our existing stock of knowledge affects how we perceive the world and predicts the consequences of our actions. In organizations, strongly held assumptions can easily block from our awareness the very feedback information that indicates important changes in the environment, which can make the embedded assumptions obsolete. Oftentimes, business firms that are in serious financial distress or have gone bankrupt are examples of organizations that blindly stuck to "business as usual" practices and misperceived the changed environment around them.

Systems thinking is all about fast and effective knowledge-building that addresses the complexity of cause and effect within a changing environment and orchestrates the discovery of root causes of problems. In the health care field, systems thinking enables us to more clearly analyze the processes by which new drugs are discovered, tested, and made available to patients.

What is the *purpose* of the new drug approval process? It is not 100 percent safety. That is impossible in the real world. Seeking to achieve it means denying millions of people access to drugs whose benefits far outweigh their risks. From the perspective of the customers of the drugs-to-patients system, the purpose, as previously noted, is to deliver better drugs, sooner, at lower cost.

We *perceive* that some people die from drugs that were approved by the FDA, and we are encouraged to conclude that this is because the FDA's approval process is insufficiently rigorous. But a systems mindset requires that we consider the far greater number of deaths and the unnecessary suffering that occur because the FDA's process is *already too rigorous*. We are not seeing the whole picture when we rely on the media's focus on the small number of deaths that may result from approved drugs.

We are attracted to simplistic public policy solutions such as price controls because we tend to use the wrong patterns for inferring *cause and effect* relationships and predicting the *consequences* of government policies. Governments around the world have tried price controls for literally thousands of years. They have never worked as expected by policy makers. Controls are evaded, they discourage production and investment, and they cause massive inefficiency. However, a policy maker who genuinely applies a systems mindset with the goal of better drugs, sooner, at lower cost would come to recognize the unintended and disastrous consequences of price controls.

As for *feedback* relevant to reform policies, we would be well-served by studying the results of off-label prescriptions, which is a limited form of the proposed Free To Choose Medicine. (Off-label use refers to instances in which doctors network informally and prescribe an approved drug to treat a condition that differs from the FDA approval specification, based on doctors' judgments of likely patient benefits and results of similar use by other doctors.) That's an important "experiment" that has been well underway for many years, yet very few people have "connected the dots" and understand its importance to the reform debate.

Finally, the *knowledge base* about new drugs has been growing rapidly in recent years. Thanks to the Internet and breakthroughs in biopharmacology, we now know much more about promising new drugs, and we can access the information much faster. Has the FDA adapted to this remarkable progress in technology in ways that meet the needs of today's patients? The answer is a resounding "No!"

Especially egregious examples of the lack of a systems mindset are commonplace in the news media, which have always seemed eager to run stories about people who have died from the use of approved drugs. Simple linear cause and effect (ignoring system complexity) seems to work well for news reporters who have to tell a "complete" story in two to three minutes. They presume the cause of people dying is that the FDA is not doing enough testing. The presumed solution is that the FDA's power should be increased so it can do even more testing.

When a systems mindset is applied to organizations, it can reveal many problems that prevent the organization from being successful. Here are three lessons learned in business that are relevant to thinking about the drug approval process:

- **Too much focus on local efficiency.** The performance of a system needs to be judged in terms of the value delivered to the end customers because that is the true purpose and justification for the overall system. It should not be judged in terms of the local efficiency of any one component of the system. Heavily focusing on making one component "perfect" can degrade the operation of the entire system.

- **Target bottlenecks instead**. A tunnel focus on improving one component of the system also blocks the vision needed to see the key system constraint, or bottleneck. Consider a manufacturing line where a systems view would indicate that the key constraint (bottleneck) is machine B. Absent a systems view, a more efficient and faster machine A (upstream from and feeding into B) is installed. Although this will improve the local performance of A, it can easily make matters worse for B, to the detriment of the overall system.

- **Avoid performance-constraining assumptions.** The root cause of the key constraint (bottleneck) often resides in an automatic or unconscious acceptance of performance-constraining assumptions embedded in a firm's (or industry's) culture or business practices. For example, until Southwest Airlines was created, the industry norm was the hub-and-spoke model for routing planes because it had been "proven" to be the most efficient way to operate planes. Instead Southwest focused on *what customers really wanted* and delivered point-to-point service by greatly expanding the number of cities served. Increased customer demand from lower fares, quick turnarounds at airports, and full planes translated into industry-leading profitability.

How Markets Work

Free To Choose Medicine involves restructuring the drugs-to-patients system to achieve the benefits obtainable from a market system. Given that, it is helpful to summarize how markets work and why they lead to a higher standard of living.

Markets are extremely complex and largely unplanned systems, and consequently they are best analyzed with a systems mindset. Generally, people do not have a deep understanding of how markets work, and as a result they have no idea of how the pharmaceutical industry operates in general, or, in particular, the relationships among companies' R&D investments, profits, and the delivery of innovative new drugs that raise the standard of care. This incomplete knowledge leads to ill-informed support for poor public policy options, such as price controls on drugs.

Briefly, and in basic terms, markets begin when there is a voluntary exchange among individuals. When exchanges are voluntary, both parties benefit, giving up something they value relatively less in order to gain something they value relatively more.

Voluntary exchange creates opportunities for specialization. That is, some individuals specialize in producing goods and services at a lower cost than others, and then trade those goods and services for things they need. Specialization and the division of labor increase productivity – output per hour worked – and lead to wealth creation. Specialization vastly increases the amount of goods exchanged.

Prices evolved as exchange moved from barter to buying and selling using currency. Prices contain information about value judgments that would otherwise remain invisible. Once we know the price of a good or service, trade can extend beyond family members to other members of the community; and, as technology allows it, to buyers and sellers throughout a country and now throughout the world.

Prices coordinate action by providing profit incentives to effectively allocate and use resources. Business enterprises respond to the profit incentive and act with the expectation of earning economic profit by efficiently providing products and services in amounts that "the market" wants. Over the long term, the bigger the gain in profits, the more value-added has been delivered to customers. The real bottom line of free-market capitalism is a rising standard of living for consumers.

However, let's be clear that free-market capitalism rightly represents an ideal condition in which a level playing field facilitates consumer choice, competition leading to business successes and failures, and resources flowing to those most skilled in efficiently meeting consumer needs. In reality, the playing field often is distorted by government loan guarantees, bailouts, "job creation" initiatives, and myriad tax laws and regulations that favor special interests. Then, in the aggregate, consumers lose and the favored few gain. This is the state of affairs in America today and it has a name: *crony capitalism*.

Nevertheless, the historical record of economic progress, or lack thereof, over many centuries offers compelling evidence that *more* free-market-oriented societies create far greater wealth compared to *less* free-market-oriented societies.[2] The freedom to buy, sell, invest, and profit is the most critical determinant of the radically different lives people experience in South Korea compared to North Korea.

Without any doubt, freedom is central to the functioning of a society's economy. The freedom to make voluntary transactions in a society with institutions that support private property rights and the rule of law enables business enterprise to flourish. This generates more wealth and a rising standard of living. And generally, more wealth translates to better health. Wealthier people and societies can minimize physical risks, get adequate food, benefit from better health and safety measures, and afford modern medical treatment for serious illnesses. Not only are people with increasing wealth better able to afford improved health care, but they are participating in an economic system in which the effectiveness of health treatments is continually improving due to innovation from private-sector drug development firms.

The wealth-creating rules of behavior of a free-market system evolve and survive over time as they are embedded in institutions. Consider the multitude of rules that comprise modern exchanges for trading stocks, bonds, and commodities. Imagine the difficulties (inefficiencies) in trading those items in the absence of exchanges whose main mission is to facilitate voluntary transactions so that buyers and sellers can better align their preferences. For example, electronic trading of stocks has enabled investors to greatly reduce the middleman (broker) transaction costs for buying and selling stocks.

In a market-based system, resources are continually moving toward those who are most skillful in anticipating consumer needs, innovating, and efficiently delivering products and services that are in demand. Over the long term, firms that are highly skilled in delivering value to customers earn higher profits than less-skilled firms. As mentioned in the previous chapter, investors provided risk capital to Dendreon based on expectations of future profits. Dendreon investors were part of a profit-seeking system that kept the firm alive and then helped to expand the firm's capabilities to deliver a breakthrough medical innovation to customers (patients). In drug development companies (e.g., biotech companies) investors routinely suffer large losses on their investments. But their losses are offset by occasional big successes.

Competition forces even very successful firms to change in ways that benefit customers, otherwise their profits decline and their survival can be threatened. William J. Baumol, a distinguished economist at New York University, provides the following description of the competitive pressure on firms in a free-market environment:

> [W]hat differentiates the prototype capitalist economy most sharply from all other economic systems is free-market pressures that force firms into a continuing process of innovation, *because it becomes a matter of life and death for many of them* …clear to historian and laypersons alike is that capitalism is unique in the extraordinary growth record it has been able to achieve; in its recurring industrial revolutions that have produced an outpouring of material wealth unlike anything previously seen in human history … it seems indisputable that innovation accounts for much of this enviable growth record … in key parts of the economy the prime weapon of competition is not price but innovation … The result is a ferocious arms race among the firms in the most rapidly evolving sectors of the economy, with innovation as the prime weapon (italics in the original).[3]

The market process involves lots of experimenting and an enormous variety of ways in which to efficiently meet customer needs. This is an uncontrolled environment of quick feedback about actions and consequences and fast-paced learning in which customers have the most important voice. Their preferences are the final arbiter of what is "best." This is profoundly important to appreciate. Failure to do so is the source of all kinds of well-intended regulatory actions that yield bad consequences.

The Role of Government in Markets

Markets, as the late economist Friedrich Hayek wrote, are *spontaneous orders* that emerge and thrive without government planning. Beyond performing essential roles in defining and enforcing private property rights and banning the use of force or fraud, government's role, according to Hayek, should be limited. Otherwise, governments end up interfering with the price-information system that works so well to create wealth and direct resources to where they are most needed.

Worthwhile regulation facilitates the wealth creation process. For example, the regulation that requires food manufacturers to plainly identify nutrition facts on the side of a box of cereal helps consumers make more informed purchase decisions. I happen to feel better off due to this rule, although this is a judgment call. Some might argue that if enough consumers wanted this information on their cereal boxes, then cereal companies would discover this preference and provide it in order to deliver a more desirable product. In theory, that may be true, but as a practical matter, my judgment is that this government-imposed rule leads to a benefit exceeding its cost.

Consider how Congress, intent on promoting a reduction in the use of petroleum-based fuels, has frequently passed legislation authorizing substantial subsidies for ethanol producers. One of many unintended consequences was skyrocketing prices for tortillas in Mexico as corn prices shot up due to a spike in demand for corn to be used in manufacturing ethanol. Cost-benefit analyses of the ethanol subsidy repeatedly concluded it is not economically justified.[4]

To cite a more extreme example, at one time, in the former Soviet Union, the Soviet bureaucracy orchestrated the production of more shoes than any other country – more than three pairs per year for every man, woman, and child. Nevertheless, there frequently were long lines of people waiting to buy the limited quantity of imported shoes.[5] The reason for this paradox was that government planners had decided what sizes and styles of shoes would be produced and the extent that imported shoes would be permitted. The point is that judging what meets the needs of people is generally best left to a market system keyed to voluntary choice and not to government bureaucracy.

So, how much regulation of new drugs is too much? Neither the FDA nor Congress knows because consumer choice is currently eliminated from our system. Instead, rigid adherence to statistical averages in the evaluation of clinical trials for tightly specified patient populations dominates approval and rejection decisions. This is the opposite of a market process that fosters great variety enabling the best solution for each customer to be selected.

FDA Clinical Trials

Prior to 1962, after successfully passing a safety test, drugs could be sold and were evaluated for effectiveness in actual use by doctors and patients. That market-based system is essentially how drugs are presently evaluated for effectiveness in the U.S. for off-label use. But legislation in 1962 granted the FDA an effective monopoly over access to new drugs. It provided that a drug developer could not market a drug until the mandated clinical trials were completed, the data submitted to the FDA, and – after lengthy analysis – FDA approval was given.

From a systems perspective, the FDA's new drug approval process is one component of a complex system that begins in the R&D laboratories of drug development companies and ends with drugs being used to help people improve their health. At a very early stage of research, a firm must select drug candidates. These decisions are enormously important to both society and the future direction of scientific work within a firm.

A firm's selection process can easily get distorted because management, due to the extremely long time before a drug can generate revenues, is hypersensitive to the statistical milestones central to future clinical trials. This can lead to a preference to fund the development of drugs that have only a marginal benefit over existing, approved treatments because they also have a lower risk of not being approved by the FDA than do cutting-edge new drugs. Moreover, small drug development firms may have a dozen potential breakthrough drugs but must bet the farm on one candidate because of the enormous cost of completing the FDA testing and approval process. With a systems mindset, we can see the relationship between enormously important, early decisions and much later FDA clinical testing requirements.

Randomized controlled trials (RCTs) are used in the later stage of the FDA's extraordinarily time-consuming and expensive testing process. Figure 2.1 provides an overview of this system with approximate timelines. It can take a decade for a new drug to make it all the way through the FDA's trials and final review. Many drugs, of course, don't make it.

Figure 2.1 Drugs-To-Patients System

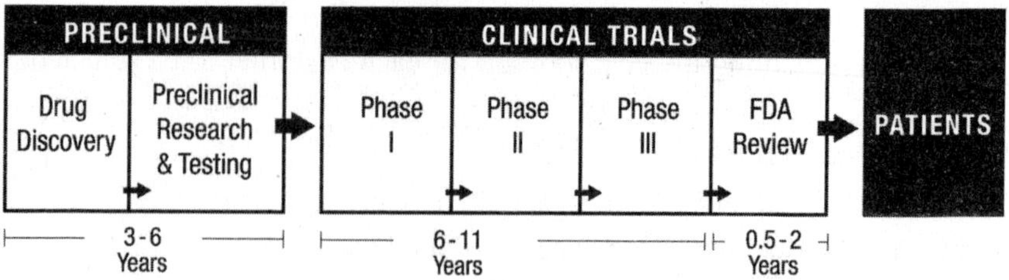

PRECLINICAL		CLINICAL TRIALS				PATIENTS
Drug Discovery	Preclinical Research & Testing	Phase I	Phase II	Phase III	FDA Review	PATIENTS

|———— 3-6 ————| |———— 6-11 ————————|— 0.5-2 —|
| Years | Years | Years |

Source: Tufts Center for the Study of Drug Development, http://csdd.tufts.edu, and the Pharmaceutical Research and Manufacturers of America, http://www.phrma.org.

The drug discovery stage produces drug compounds that show some initial promise. Historically, a universe of 5,000 compounds in the drug discovery stage typically yields 250 candidates that move to the preclinical stage involving synthesis and purification plus animal testing. This sample is further reduced to about five especially promising drugs for which an IND (Investigational New Drug) application is filed with the FDA. Upon IND approval and Institutional Review Board approvals at the test sites, a developmental drug can begin human clinical testing consisting of three phases. Of every five drugs entering clinical testing, on average only one drug receives FDA approval.

In Phase I, 20 to 100 volunteers participate in trials designed to assess drug safety and initial dosing ranges. In Phase II, drug efficacy and side effects are evaluated with 100 to 500 patients who have the specified target disease or condition. Expanded controlled and uncontrolled trials in Phase III typically involve 1,000 to 5,000 patients at multiple sites. Phase III is the most comprehensive of the three phases and is designed to further evaluate safety and efficacy.

Upon completion of Phase III and believing the results are sufficiently favorable, the developer may submit an NDA (New Drug Application) to the FDA in hopes of securing an approval to market the drug. If approval is granted, the FDA may require a Phase IV study to gather additional information about safety and effectiveness.

The total average cost to develop an approved drug is close to a billion dollars today, including expenditures for drug discovery and preclinical work and, of course, for a great many clinical trials throughout the three-phase process. This total necessarily includes the costs of failed drugs, which are an integral part of securing approval for a successful drug. About half of the total cost is due to the drug developer's capital being tied up for such a lengthy time without generating income.[6]

For insights into the FDA's mindset, Henry Miller, M.D., a physician, molecular biologist, and public policy analyst who formerly held high-level positions within the FDA, provides this first-hand account of the pressures and incentives that face FDA staff:

> Another aspect of self-interest pertains to regulators' fear of being perceived as too eager to approve new products. In the early 1980s, when I headed the team at the FDA that was reviewing the NDA [New Drug Application] for recombinant human insulin, the first drug made with gene-splicing techniques, we were ready to recommend approval a mere four months after the application was submitted (at a time when the average time for NDA review was more than two and a half years). With quintessential bureaucratic reasoning, my supervisor refused to sign off on the approval – even though he agreed that the data provided compelling evidence of the drug's safety and effectiveness. "If anything goes wrong," he argued, "think how bad it will look that we approved the drug so quickly." (When the supervisor went on vacation, I convinced his boss to sign off on the approval.) The supervisor was more concerned with not looking bad in case of an unforeseen mishap than with getting an important new product to patients who needed it. This system lacks predictability, fairness, and integrity, but given the existing incentives and disincentives, risks and rewards, at the FDA, an official's decision to put self-interest above the public interest is hardly surprising.[7]

Sam Kazman, an attorney with the Competitive Enterprise Institute, a Washington, DC-based think tank, says the experience reported by Dr. Miller is commonplace inside FDA:

> From FDA commissioner to the bureau heads to the individual NDA reviewers, the message is clear: if you approve a drug with unanticipated side effects, both you and the agency will face the heat of newspaper headlines, television coverage and congressional hearings. On the other hand, if FDA insists on more and more data from a manufacturer, and finally approves a drug, which should have been on the market months or years before, there is no such price to pay. Drug lag's victims and their families will hardly be complaining, because they won't know what hit them … They only know that there is nothing their doctors can do for them. From the standpoint of … politics, they are invisible.[8]

Not surprisingly, rapidly advancing medical knowledge, coupled to personalized medicine (drugs that are tailored to a patient's genetic makeup), now is jamming the "front door" of the FDA's drug approval process. Since that process can take as long as a decade, many of the drugs the FDA finally approves will already be obsolete, i.e., demonstrably inferior to new drugs just starting the review process or slowly making their way along it.

The FDA Bottleneck

Dr. Miller's devastating account of decision-making inside the FDA is Exhibit One in support of the case that the FDA is currently a dysfunctional system. The consensus opinion of economists who have studied the impact of the steady trend of increasing FDA demands for ever-more expensive and time-consuming clinical trials is that the costs to society have far exceeded the benefits.[9]

If we stand back and observe the landscape, how would we characterize the thinking template used by FDA officials and many members of Congress who have oversight responsibility for the FDA? For sure, they do not use a systems mindset to get them focused on the true purpose of the approval process: better drugs, sooner, at lower cost. Applying the three lessons from a systems mindset mentioned at the start of this chapter to the FDA suggests that:

- The FDA's focus on the *local efficiency* of its clinical trials yields a mindset that is blind to a potential reorganization that could uproot ingrained assumptions and lead to major performance improvements.

- The FDA testing process itself is the *bottleneck*, or key system constraint, that holds back large-scale progress aimed at the true goal of the system.

- An *implicit assumption* by the FDA is that, to do its job well, it must be able to set and enforce ever-more-stringent requirements for clinical trials.

The more one examines how the FDA functions, the more apparent becomes its actual foremost goal – to avoid negative publicity due to adverse side effects from approved drugs. Evidently, in the mind of the

FDA staff, this goal has become synonymous with the public good and this enables the FDA to disregard the suffering and deaths due to extended delays in allowing access to new drugs.

Defenders of the FDA oftentimes point out that it is the role of Congress to pass legislation that will benefit patients, which presumably becomes the FDA's marching orders. In fact, legislation has been passed at times to accelerate drug approval, but with little real long-term effect. The key question is: Who writes the regulations that implement the legislation? The FDA, of course. The historical record shows that subsequent FDA regulations that "interpreted" the intent of legislation invariably expanded the ability of the FDA to do what it wanted to do.[10] Moreover, there is no check or balancing mechanism that weighs the costs of ever-more regulation.

A system that involves people is out of balance and ineffective when its incentives are misaligned. For example, there is little incentive for the FDA to effectively operate its "compassionate use" program. This is a program for people who have a life-threatening illness with "no comparable or satisfactory alternative drug or other therapy available to treat that stage of the disease in the intended patient population" (in the words of FDA regulations). The FDA's real motive is to encourage patients to enroll in clinical trials. But, the more promising a new developmental drug is and the more serious an illness, the more motivated patients are to avoid a clinical trial. Patients would rather attempt to gain access via the compassionate use avenue, which the FDA does not want.

Mark Thornton, a former medical reviewer in the oncology division at the FDA, says,

> I can attest to the burden the physician-sponsors of these requests have to go through with FDA reviewers as they run the gauntlet. Manufacturing, pharmacology, toxicology, pharmacokinetic, clinical and even statistical 'issues' raised by FDA staff, aimed at the applying physician, can sometimes rival receipt of an audit from the IRS. Requests are on occasion withdrawn by exasperated doctors or refused by the FDA, leaving patients to fend for themselves.[11]

Drug developers are keenly aware of the long shadow of FDA scrutiny for adverse side effects from compassionate use by patients. Because of this, drug developers typically are not enthusiastic about agreeing to a compassionate use that could put their entire approval process at greater risk.

Patients have widely varying health conditions, genetic profiles, and risk preferences. New drugs may fall short of the statistical bar set by the FDA based on the average of all patients in a clinical trial, yet be highly effective for a subset of patients in a trial. Moreover, learning takes place during clinical trials leading to plausible hypotheses (e.g., genetic factors) about why a subset of patients had a particularly robust response.

The FDA's position has been that the design and conduct of any clinical trial must not be altered by things learned during a particular clinical trial, but rather such learning is grounds for a new clinical trial. A small biotech company might very well be unable to afford a new trial. And even if a new trial is financed, patient access is delayed again for years.

The entire FDA testing and approval process is not operated to produce better drugs, sooner, at lower cost for the benefit of existing and future patients. Rather, it is clear that the status quo system is designed to make it easier for the FDA to make and defend its drug approval decisions. It operates under the belief that long delays are necessary for adequate scientific testing. The plight of existing patients who are denied access is rationalized as the necessary price to be paid in order to benefit future patients.

In the private sector, how long would a company survive if it cared so little for its current customers? In a competitive business environment, companies tend to aggressively bid for key employees with the skill sets to innovate and continually improve business processes. An intensity to serve today's customers is absent from how the FDA currently operates. For example, consider the very critical review of FDA capabilities presented in a November 2007 report by the FDA Science Board, titled *FDA Science and Mission at Risk*:

> FDA's inability to keep up with scientific advances means that American lives are at risk. While the world of drug discovery and development has undergone revolutionary change – shifting from cellular to molecular and gene-based approaches – FDA's evaluation methods have remained largely unchanged over the last half century.
>
> … FDA's failure to retain and motivate its workforce puts FDA's mission at risk. Inadequately trained scientists are generally risk-averse, and tend to give no decision, a slow decision or even worse, the wrong decision on regulatory approval or disapproval.[12]

The FDA is like another organization that has long been insulated from competition, the U.S. Postal Service. Are there any signs there of extraordinary intensity (commonplace in the private sector) to innovate to better serve customers? Not really. The arrival of competition in the form of FedEx finally forced the Post Office to improve since customers have a choice as to where to take packages that need fast delivery.

Conclusion

How does a regulatory body become so insulated that it can disregard the pleas of suffering and dying people who are being denied potentially life-saving treatments? It is the result of a lack of organized and effective opposition by the victims of horribly misguided public policy.

The victims haven't been entirely silent (or silenced). During the late 1980s, AIDs activists embarrassed the FDA sufficiently to gain faster access to some drugs. The vocal opposition by those with advanced prostate cancer was described in Chapter 1. And the parents and friends of Abigail Burroughs, Kianna Karnes, and other victims have been outspoken.

One conclusion from reading FDA innovation studies (see http://www.fda.gov) is that the FDA theme is *non-disruptive* change that clearly maintains the agency's core bureaucratic machinery. Such a *controlled environment* is the diametric opposite of innovation in the business world in which disruption of the old, obsolete ways of doing things leads to game-changing new ways to benefit customers.

Many business firms are in the "arms race" to develop innovative solutions to customer needs, as noted earlier by Baumol, but the FDA is sailing its innovation ship with its anchor dragging on the bottom. That anchor is the agency's hyper-concern with avoiding the possibility that an approved drug will show unexpected, serious adverse side effects that will be reported by the news media.

Chapter 3
Analyzing the FDA's Defenses

[T]he single most powerful explanation for how the FDA works is ... the bureaucratic imperative that seeks to expand turf no matter what its consequences for others.

Richard A. Epstein
Overdose: How Excessive Government Regulation Stifles Pharmaceutical Innovation (2006)

Supporters of the FDA's current policies say the assessment of whether a drug is safe and effective demands randomized controlled trials (RCTs), because they are the gold standard of scientific testing. They say any proposal that could disrupt the FDA's ability to conduct RCTs is unacceptable. Moreover, they say the public is incapable of making informed decisions about whether to use not-yet-FDA-approved drugs, and that many drugs fail to win FDA approval. Let's follow their arguments and see where they come up short.

The Gold Standard

Participants in an RCT are selected at random (by chance alone) to receive one of several interventions. In a typical RCT, one intervention is a new drug treatment and the other is a standard of comparison (or control), which can be conventional practice, a placebo (sugar pill), or no intervention at all. An RCT is a powerful, quantitative measure to compare outcomes after the participants receive the interventions.

In his 1935 book, *The Design of Experiments*, R.A. Fisher explains the importance of using random samples to minimize biases such as any preconceptions by individual experimenters. His work was a major breakthrough for scientific testing and helped to create the foundation of modern statistical analysis.

The first methodologically rigorous application of randomization in a clinical trial of therapeutic drugs was orchestrated by Austin Bradford Hill in 1946.[1] The purpose of that trial was to determine the effect of streptomycin on tuberculosis. Of the 107 patients admitted, 55 were assigned to the streptomycin group and the remaining 52 allocated to a control group with only bed rest. After six months, 7 percent of the streptomycin patients died compared to 27 percent in the control group. The statistical probability of such a positive result for the drug being tested due to chance alone was less than one in a hundred.

The FDA's Mantra

The FDA has a masterful track record of gaining ever-more domination over drug developers and patients. Its staff justifies their actions by continually posing what appears to be a simple question: Do you want citizens to have safe and effective drugs? Receiving no disagreement, they contend the next logical step is greater FDA power and a bigger budget to get the job done.

Richard Epstein, a professor of law at the University of Chicago, captured how strongly ingrained the FDA's perception of reality is as well as the significant challenge to motivate Congress to fundamentally reform the FDA:

> My own sense, therefore, is that any proposed system of decentralization could work only if the government removed the oversight from the FDA, with its ingrained habits ... But in light of the FDA's rearguard efforts to maintain its own power against other initiatives, and the knee-jerk reaction in Congress for imposing stultifying drug regulation, the betting is that the future holds only more of the same. It is amazing the harm that can be done if the elimination of patient choice is regarded as proof of a diligent system of consumer protection![2]

To disregard the costs of testing and approval is to abandon the fundamental and appropriate goal of better drugs, sooner, at lower cost, which is even an integral part of the FDA's own mission statement. *Safe and effective drugs* may work well as a sound bite on the nightly news, but it is a smokescreen that diverts attention from the FDA's massive underperformance as regards drugs being delivered *sooner, at lower cost.*

No drug is 100 percent safe. Aspirin can lead, especially in elderly people, to hospitalization and death due to gastrointestinal bleeding and perforation.[3] "Effective," as John Calfee explained in Chapter 1, is a judgment about the tradeoff that only patients can make. "They are the only ones who can balance quality-of-life against the risk of death. Their view should be absolutely paramount."[4]

Now, the FDA may conclude that a recently approved drug is effective compared to existing treatments and patients should be pleased. But when compared to a potential breakthrough drug making its way through a decade of FDA testing and analysis, a recently approved drug could already be obsolete. And many patients denied the freedom to use the new drug being tested, especially if they are on death's doorstep, are poorly served.

Further, the simplistic slogan of safe and effective drugs diverts attention away from the basic tradeoff issue facing the FDA: More extensive and hugely expensive testing may reduce the probability of unanticipated adverse side effects from an approved drug, but at the same time also greatly increases drug costs to consumers and, most importantly, causes suffering and premature deaths from delayed access. That's the tradeoff dilemma.

One plausible motivation behind the FDA's ironclad allegiance to RCTs is being able to say: "We used the most rigorous scientific tool to guide our decision as to whether a drug is safe and effective." However, we need to dig deeper and better understand why Dr. Richard Pazdur, head of the FDA's cancer drug office and often referred to as the "cancer czar," made the following point about the limitations of Phase II trials and the need for RCTs at a March 12, 2003 Oncologic Drugs Advisory Committee meeting:

> ... [T]here is a mantra, adequate and well-controlled trials, adequate and well-controlled trials, adequate and well-controlled trials. I am mentioning that three times, because I think that is at the heart of the question.[5]

To no surprise, patient advocacy groups like the Abigail Alliance lock horns with Dr. Pazdur and argue that the needs of patients fighting a terminal illness should be given top priority. But the FDA has a different agenda. There seem to be three possible reasons why the FDA maintains its steadfast opposition to allow early access to the most promising drugs:

(1) If a promising drug were made accessible and resulted in particularly serious side effects, the FDA would be hit with negative publicity.

(2) The FDA either believes, or wants the public to believe, that the most promising drugs cannot be determined before Phase III is completed and all clinical trial data have been analyzed by the FDA as part of the NDA.

(3) Making the most promising new drugs available would be the crack in the dam that would eventually force a major restructuring of RCT requirements. Since RCTs help the FDA make tough approval calls where it is genuinely very difficult to decide which way to go, they don't want to give them up.

As for reason (1), the Dual Tracking proposal explained in the next chapter would take the heat off the FDA with respect to negative publicity. Patients and doctors would be fully informed of up-to-date treatment results, including adverse side effects, and patients would be empowered to take personal responsibility for the use of not-yet-approved drugs. This recognizes that seizing new opportunities for health improvement requires relevant information and comes with risk.

Reason (2) is at odds with the experience of many people who are knowledgeable about ongoing clinical trials. Many respected and knowledgeable doctors reach informed opinions on the efficacy of medicines that have not completed Phase III trials. Keep in mind that we are talking about the most promising new drugs in the pipeline. As of this writing, the Abigail Alliance has waged battles with the FDA to expedite access to 17 developmental drugs for patients on death's doorstep who were unable to enroll in clinical trials. All 17 drugs were subsequently approved by the FDA.[6]

Reason (2) is weak now and getting even weaker because of continual advancements in data management technology (coupled to the Internet) that can deliver to patients and doctors up-to-date analyses of all treatment results for new drugs.

Reason (3) will be rebutted at greater length on the following pages. But as a summary, that some patients should suffer and die without a choice of medical treatment in order that some people have an easier time at their jobs is a reason equal parts tragedy and outrage. The injustice and inhumanity of it ought to make Free To Choose Medicine a front-burner political issue.

When Are Randomized Controlled Trials Unethical?

RCTs raise ethical questions. "Equipoise" is the concept that an RCT should satisfy the criterion of collective uncertainty about the superiority of the treatment being evaluated. The fundamental principle is that it would be unethical to knowingly keep a patient from receiving a superior treatment. Equipoise, coupled to the informed consent of clinical trial patients, is the rationale used by the FDA and those who claim RCTs are ethical. Those who believe with a high degree of confidence that the drug being tested is superior to a comparison drug or placebo can claim, by the equipoise criterion, that the trial is unethical.[7]

On the one side stands the FDA setting a very high standard for what constitutes sufficient evidence of a benefit. The FDA staff has no incentive to lower that bar and plenty of reasons to keep it high. FDA, therefore, can be counted on to demand completion of RCTs of maximum practical size and duration before a new drug is approved.

On the other side stand doctors, many of them more highly qualified than those in the employ of the FDA. They are the ones with first-hand knowledge of their patients' symptoms and with access to real-time data from their own patients, other doctors in their clinic or hospital, or doctors in their practice groups. These doctors may rightly believe they are better positioned than the FDA to determine when sufficient evidence of a benefit has been achieved and, oftentimes, they are justified to believe it is unethical to put their patients in a clinical trial and risk possibly receiving an inferior control group treatment.

This argument impresses most of us, I believe; but in the end the FDA has the final say. It has a legal monopoly and is not deterred by claims of unethical behavior. The real issue is not splitting hairs in judging clinical equipoise; rather it is the lack of freedom of choice to do what one believes is in his or her best interest.

Try this Thought Experiment

Opponents to consumer choice invariably argue that it cannot be permitted because it would interfere with enrollment in randomized controlled trials. Their assumption is that while RCTs may be unethical for today's patients who would receive inferior treatments due to being assigned to an unlucky arm of a trial, this ethical shortcoming is acceptable because of the expected growth in knowledge that presumably will benefit future patients.

That assumption appears to be accepted without question by the FDA's defenders. However, it is doubtful that many of today's patients or their families would agree with the assumed necessity of their becoming sacrificial lambs. For that matter, if compelled to vote up or down on this issue, how many politicians would support the use of unethical clinical trials for the sake of better statistical evidence?

And, as a historical aside, during the clinical trial of streptomycin referred to earlier, a senior physician contracted tuberculosis. He was able to secure streptomycin outside of the trial. "In this brief instance of medical history, the equipoise, the ethical arguments, and all other justifications for providing treatment by chance, were thrown out the window in favor of the human factor …"[8]

As discussed earlier, consumer choice obviates the need for abstract arguments about equipoise. A thought experiment puts this distinction into sharper focus. Let's say a new experimental drug, Alpha, is to be tested against drug Beta in an RCT. Patients, advised by their doctors, have the freedom of choice to purchase Alpha from the drug developer or to enter the RCT with a 50/50 chance of receiving either Alpha or Beta. People choosing to enter the RCT would receive free drugs. Finally, assume the patients and doctors have access to up-to-date information on treatment results (including adverse side effects) for both Alpha and Beta.

If so many patients choose to purchase Alpha that there are too few patients for the clinical trial to be conducted, how should those results be interpreted?

The first message of the results is that, based on the advice of their doctors, a large number of patients believe Alpha is the superior treatment and they do not want to accept the risk of receiving Beta. Patients would have voted with their feet, leaving no ambiguity as might arise in an abstract debate about equipoise. The fact that choosing Alpha would require paying the drug developer for the drug, rather than getting free drugs by being part of a clinical trial, indicates an especially strong opinion about the perceived superiority of Alpha. If patients and their doctors perceived Alpha and Beta to be equals, there would not be a clinical trial enrollment shortfall, as sufficient numbers of patients would enroll in the trial to avoid the cost of purchasing Alpha.

The proper interpretation is that RCT enrollment is problematic for the FDA only when most patients and doctors disagree with the regulating body's judgment of the risks and comparative benefits of a new drug. When there is widespread doubt about the efficacy of a new drug, patients would be expected to enroll in RCTs without grave concern about which drug they will receive.

The standard argument that freedom of choice is unacceptable because it could threaten clinical trial enrollment is short-sighted. It tolerates an environment in which existing patients are forced to put themselves at risk of receiving an inferior treatment. This is a clear case of flawed thinking focusing on local efficiency (operation of RCTs) to the detriment of existing patients.

This thought experiment differs from the choices patients and doctors make in the real world in two ways. First, patients and doctors currently are not free to go around RCTs in order to gain access to new drugs. Second, and importantly, patients, doctors, and the FDA do not have equal access to up-to-date information about treatment results because there is no widely shared database for observational data and because results of RCTs are not made available in ways that would enable patients and their doctors to use them.

These differences between a world where patients and doctors have information and are free to choose new drugs and the current world where patients are forced to enroll in trials where they may receive a placebo or inferior treatment direct our attention to the reforms that need to be made to fix the drug approval process. Patients need to be free to choose, and they and their doctors need a reliable source of information about treatment outcomes. These two reforms – Dual Tracking that provides a Free To Choose Track for early access to new drugs and a Tradeoff Evaluation Database – are discussed in detail in Chapter 4.

Observational Data versus Randomized Controlled Trials

While we should appreciate the power of RCTs as a scientific tool in general, the systems mindset reminds us that learning is a complex process occurring in uncontrolled environments as well as in controlled experiments such as RCTs. A person's base of knowledge can be and is expanded all the time from sources that fall short of a "gold standard." In fact, if we held out for evidence that met that standard in most parts of our lives, we would be nearly frozen in place, unable to act for want of sufficiently good information.

Observational data representing treatment results for a specific drug for patients outside of the controlled environment of a clinical trial offer an enormous and rapidly growing source of knowledge. Observational data are already prevalent in communications among doctors about the pros and cons of off-label use of approved drugs.

Consider this case. Some Australians with cystic fibrosis (CF) reported to their doctors that their airways felt clearer after surfing in the ocean. This observation led to the hypothesis that inhaling salt spray could be beneficial to those suffering from CF because salt might help restore a thin lubricant layer of water that normally coats airway surfaces. This hypothesis was testable with a straightforward RCT. It did not involve ethical concerns as would occur when those on death's doorstep are put at risk of receiving a placebo or a clearly inferior treatment because of an unlucky assignment to the "wrong" arm of an RCT. In this situation, RCTs confirmed the efficacy of inhaling a fine spray of salt water.[9]

Oftentimes, the usefulness of RCTs is in disconfirming a strongly held hypothesis. For illustrative purposes, let's assume a hypothetical situation in which the benefit received after surfing was actually due to extended exposure to sunlight that jumpstarted production of vitamin D that somehow led to improved breathing. Sunlight would then be labeled a confounding variable. Salt spray and improved breathing would be merely correlated with one another and it would be a mistake to imply a cause and effect relationship.

Back to our hypothetical example, a properly designed RCT would reveal the lack of causality; i.e., salt spray does no better than a placebo spray. The RCT could warrant this conclusion more precisely and with far fewer patients than an uncontrolled sample of patients using salt spray only. But it would not help to pinpoint the critical role of extended exposure to sunlight. Potentially, that could be discovered by observations of changes in breathing that accompany significant change in exposure to the sun (e.g., a winter vacation in Florida).

Observational data (with associated inferences of cause and effect) do not have the rigor of data produced by RCTs, yet it is by observation, not RCTs, that we build up most of our knowledge base as we experience daily life. Surgical advances are achieved in this manner without RCTs. Medical devices, such as artificial hearts, are not subject to RCTs. Not even the FDA would demand the insertion of placebo artificial hearts into patients since the "cost" would be absurd, not to mention the immediate moral outrage that would ensue.

Conclusion

The more one looks at how uncertainty is handled in the real world of patients who are motivated to improve their health, the more suspect becomes the FDA's presumption that the world of new drugs is too complex for patients to handle effectively. Patients and their doctors are already grappling with the uncertainties of illnesses, including the evaluation of the risk-reward for new drugs, by sharing information online and experimenting with off-label prescriptions.

The FDA's position is indefensible. Its policies inflict too high a cost on existing patients from delayed access to new drugs in order to protect the FDA's staff from criticism on the chance they miss some negative side effects of an approved drug. They can dress this up as "the demands of high science" or "the needs of future patients," but on closer examination as we have done here, neither argument is impressive.

With the rapid growth of new information and new drugs being discovered, we need competition so that patients have a means to circumvent the FDA's business-as-usual process with its decade-long testing and analysis. Such competition would finally provide feedback as to the real usefulness of the FDA process and almost certainly force the FDA to radically streamline its current process.

Ask yourself if today's variety and capabilities of cell phones would exist if we had maintained the business-as-usual monopolies over phone service. There would have been no "arms race among firms ... with innovation as the prime weapon."

In its sheltered cocoon where customers have no voice, the FDA ignores its true mission and the public's true interests. Instead, it focuses on local efficiency that translates into a mantra that drug approval is to be based on the strongest statistical testing possible. The FDA itself has become the critical bottleneck in the nation's health care system. It's time to end the FDA's deadly hold on the nation's supply of new drugs.

Chapter 4
Free To Choose Medicine

Choice is an element in freedom and there can be no choice without unrealized and precarious possibilities.

John Dewey
Human Nature and Conduct (1922)

This chapter describes the Free To Choose Medicine reform proposal to break the FDA's monopoly on access to new drugs and restore our freedom of choice in medicine. The reform has three components: creation of a Free To Choose Track separate from the FDA for people who want early access to promising new drugs and who are willing to accept what could be higher risk; creation of a Tradeoff Evaluation Database (TED) to capture and make widely available real-time data on drug effects; and "conditional approval," a new level of FDA regulatory approval for new drugs.

Summary of the Case for Reform

Before getting into the tall weeds of this reform plan, let's summarize the core arguments so far.[1]

- We all want healthier, longer, and more productive lives for ourselves and our family members.

- The primary goal of the FDA's regulatory process should be to deliver better drugs, sooner, at lower cost.

- Under the current FDA monopolistic regime, the FDA demands more-extensive and ever-more-expensive clinical testing. This is accompanied by an out-of-balance, too extreme focus on safety in order to minimize any negative publicity from occurrences of adverse side effects after drugs have been approved. The goals of "sooner, at lower cost" have been pushed aside.

- As it presently functions, the FDA is a bottleneck in the drugs-to-patients system – unnecessarily delaying the approval of new drugs by many years as well as stifling innovation. People are suffering and dying because they are denied timely access to new drugs stuck in the FDA pipeline and because excessively expensive testing requirements reduce drug development firms' research budgets. Although not reported on the nightly news, the result is an enormous invisible graveyard of those who were, and are, and will be, denied access.

Due to political and institutional incentives, the FDA won't reform itself. The way to solve the bottleneck is to break the FDA's monopoly on new drug approval by *legislating a path around the FDA* so that patients and doctors are free to choose. I call this Dual Tracking.

With Dual Tracking, on one track drug developers proceed with the conventional FDA clinical trials and approval process. On a separate, Free To Choose Track, drug developers whose drugs have successfully passed their safety trials and generated preliminary efficacy data can elect to sell their drugs to patients and their doctors. A combination of government oversight for a Tradeoff Evaluation Database and private-sector information providers would ensure that patients and doctors are well-informed.

Instead of the current one-size-fits-all regulatory straitjacket that assumes everyone is equally risk-averse, patients could express their own unique preferences for risk, guided by their doctors' and their own judgments about pain, the limited ability to work or perform daily chores, and the opportunity for health improvement decisions that only they can make. Patients could elect to use only approved drugs, which are very safe. No one is forced to accept less-safe drugs.

A Tradeoff Evaluation Database (TED) would be created so patients and their doctors have Internet access to up-to-date information about the risks and comparative effectiveness of approved and not-yet-approved drugs. Pharmaceutical companies also would have access to this new treasure trove of data, greatly speeding up innovation through faster learning and a better allocation of research and development funds.

In the future, competition from Dual Tracking would compel the FDA to streamline its clinical testing and approval process, yielding substantial reductions in the costs to drug developers of gaining FDA approvals. In turn, this could lead to substantial reductions in prescription drug prices.

The Free To Choose Medicine Act

Truly large-scale performance improvements that benefit the customers of a system frequently require abandoning conventional assumptions that have been a traditional part of an organization's culture. That is why, in the private sector, the support of CEOs and the boards of directors of business firms is necessary to orchestrate major structural change even though employees may resist it. Resistance to breaking a business-as-usual mindset inside an organization can initially be expected until big gains in performance are demonstrated.

Especially strong resistance to change occurs when employees have defined their jobs in terms of achieving what we have referred to as local efficiency. The shared culture of FDA managers considers safe and effective drugs as their goal, with RCTs as their most powerful tool – regardless of how this interferes with the more appropriate customer-centric goal of better drugs, sooner, at lower cost. It is highly unlikely that FDA management would lead or voluntarily embrace a reorganization that would enable patients to circumvent the testing and approval process.

Unless Congress restructures the FDA by law, there will be bitter and unending conflicts between the agency and patients who suffer from a lack of choice – conflicts rooted in cross-purposes. More conflicts will arise between the FDA and drug developers who want to learn as much, as quickly as possible, about fundamental disease mechanisms and related ways to design drugs to treat and cure disease. Meanwhile, these pharmaceutical firms are devoting enormous time, talent, and money to meet FDA statistical milestones in ways that are less than optimal for fast learning and adaptation. These conflicts center on many of the operational difficulties in running clinical trials.

Reform requires Congress to pass, and the president to sign, a Free To Choose Medicine Act, which has three key objectives: First, to permit patients, advised by their doctors, to contract with drug developers to purchase designated Free To Choose drugs and take personal responsibility for adverse side effects. Second, to create a database of drug treatment effects that gives patients and their doctors sufficient information to be able to make informed decisions. That would form the basis for granting immunity to drug developers, doctors, and related parties from strict product liability lawsuits due to adverse side effects from Free To Choose drugs. Immunity would not apply in situations of fraud or genuine negligence. Third, to authorize the FDA to grant conditional approval to promising new drugs.

For many of us, voluntary contracts would not seem to pose any thorny problems – let parties agree to a contract that each believes will be beneficial. The patient receives an opportunity to gain a health improvement not otherwise available and accepts the risk of using a new drug that is not yet approved by the FDA. The drug developer receives payment for its new drug and gains additional knowledge from observational data associated with an expanded early use of the drug. Although voluntary contracting is straightforward for most products and services, legislation is needed to overcome a hurdle in medical contracts that makes liability waivers unenforceable when the patient is deemed to have insufficient information relative to that of the service provider.[2]

Whereas medical malpractice and other forms of negligence liability arise when a patient is injured by the conduct of a physician or other health service provider who fails to exercise reasonable care, liability for adverse side effects of drugs is governed under the more exacting standard of "strict product liability." That is, a drug developer may be held liable for a patient's serious side effects even if the developer exercised all proper care in the preparation and sale of the product. This is so even with drugs that have been approved by the FDA, and under current law, courts will not honor a contractual waiver of liability, even one signed by a fully informed patient.

The core legal position laid out in the *Restatement (Third) of Torts: Products and Liability* (a widely-followed publication of the American Law Institute that guides judges and lawyers) is that "It is presumed that the ordinary product user or consumer lacks sufficient information and bargaining power to execute a fair contractual limitation of rights to recover."[3]

Richard Epstein has a different view: ""[T]he *Restatement* position is wholly undefended. ... [Its] undocumented conclusion on so critical an issue is, and should be treated as, a public travesty – it is the work of an official committee intent on preserving the bar's lucrative concession over product liability cases under the banner of consumer protection."[4]

Although it is well known that there is no such thing as a totally safe drug, developers are unlikely to make new drugs in clinical testing available through a Free To Choose Track if they could be held liable for all side effects even if they were not negligent in developing, testing, or manufacturing the drugs. Consequently, a Free To Choose Medicine Act requires Congress to pass legislation permitting patients to contractually waive their right to sue drug developers under strict product liability as long as developers do not provide false or misleading information.

Dual Tracking

Consumer choice brings competition, and that would disrupt business as usual for the FDA monopoly. Consumer choice would accelerate the pace of innovation, not only for drug developers, but also for the FDA itself. Consumer choice is what Dual Tracking is based on. Establishing a Free To Choose Track, separate from the FDA, is the practical way to implement freedom of choice.[5]

The idea is illustrated in Figure 4.1. On one track, a new drug continues with the conventional FDA testing that can easily consume a decade to complete clinical trials and possibly secure FDA approval. On a new, separate track – a Free To Choose Track, which is independent of the FDA – patients, advised by their doctors, can make informed decisions either to use an approved drug or to contract with a drug developer to buy a not-yet-approved drug. The drug developer would need to elect to place the drug on the Free To Choose Track and that drug must have passed the midpoint of its Phase II testing so there would be an early indication of its risk and effectiveness. Patients who opt for the Free To Choose Track could gain quicker access by five years or so compared to waiting for possible FDA approval.

Figure 4.1 Dual Tracking

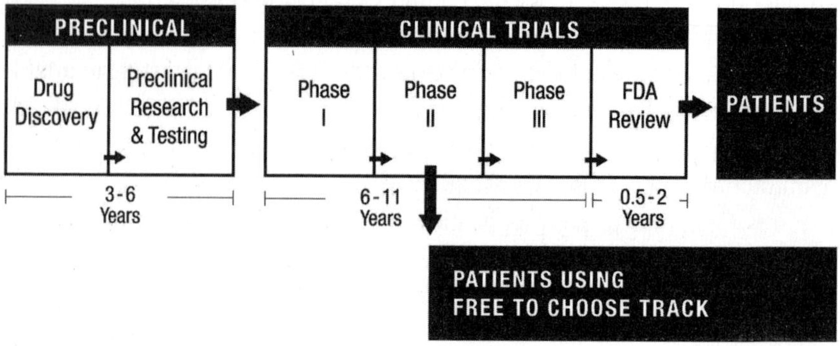

Underlying Dual Tracking is the fact, demonstrated in many other areas of commerce and human activity, that consumers are generally better off in an environment that enables them to make and take responsibility for the decisions that affect their interests.

Creating a Tradeoff Evaluation Database (TED)

For us to be able to judge if the benefit from a new drug may exceed the benefit from an approved drug and be worth the risk – i.e., for us to be informed sufficiently enough to be able to evaluate the tradeoff – we and our doctors would need relevant, up-to-date information. The information would be best accessible on the Internet in a Tradeoff Evaluation Database (TED), as shown in Figure 4.2.

The legislation to implement Dual Tracking should specify that participation on the Free To Choose Track requires not only that doctors input treatment results, but also that patients permit doctors to transmit the patient's genetic data and biomarker information to TED. Over time, this would create a treasure trove of public data that would greatly benefit pharmaceutical research.

At no charge, the government-operated TED would provide the basic information that patients and doctors need to make an informed decision about what is in patients' best interests. Private-sector companies (e.g., Google, Microsoft, IBM, and the like) would have a profit incentive to assemble and sell customized "consumer reports" that would further help patients and doctors. Consumer reports would be well-suited to pinpointing

Figure 4.2 Tradeoff Evaluation Database

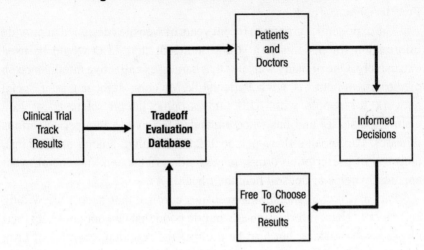

subsets of patients who are most likely and least likely to benefit, forecasting the probability of eventual FDA approval, and providing head-to-head comparisons of Free To Choose drugs and relevant FDA-approved drugs.[6]

The Dual Track environment created by combining the Free To Choose Track with TED would differ sharply from the FDA clinical trial environment. One important way is its focus on experimentation and fast-paced learning, which utilizes doctors' knowledge of each patient's unique health condition. In this unregulated environment, reports of unanticipated adverse side effects would quickly become available to patients and their doctors so they could be factored into their subsequent tradeoff evaluations and usage decisions.

Reports of the effects of new drugs from the Free To Choose Track would be different from those of randomized control trials in two main ways. First, with observational data, reported effects (both good and bad) can be influenced by causes other than the drug being taken because the population of users lacks the strict homogeneity of clinical trial populations. Thus, far more treatment results (compared to randomized control trials) are needed to support an inference that a new drug is helpful. Second, the Free To Choose Track would not exclude patients for the reasons they are denied access to clinical trials. This means that very sick patients who would not qualify for participation in a clinical trial could gain access to a drug on the Free To Choose Track.

The exponential growth in recent years of websites designed to provide information for patients is a strong indicator that TED would be used extensively. One of many websites that harnesses collective intelligence on medical treatments is www.PatientsLikeMe.com. It began as a social network for people with ALS (amyotrophic lateral sclerosis, or Lou Gehrig's disease) and has since expanded to cover a number of serious illnesses. Participants share personal data including, among other things, their use of prescription drugs, related side effects and, in general, what apparently helps or doesn't help their health.

PatientsLikeMe and similar websites confirm that people are willing and eager to share information as a public good that can not only help their own decision-making but also help direct the research activities of drug developers. It is noteworthy that drug developers and other scientific organizations purchase data from PatientsLikeMe because this kind of observational data can generate new ideas beyond those gained in their laboratories.

For example, lithium is a drug that doctors often prescribe for ALS patients although there is substantial uncertainty as to its effectiveness. An up-to-date and easy-to-understand summary of lithium treatment outcomes is maintained on the website. Membership in the lithium patients group is very large compared to typical clinical trial enrollments and is stratified by various criteria that could aid in discovering valuable insights as to who might benefit the most, or the least, from using lithium.

TED would be a PatientsLikeMe on steroids, but with more reliable data because the data would come from doctors instead of patients. Doctors would be responsible for inputting treatment results and related patient medical information. The experience of PatientsLikeMe also suggests there would be a demand for consumer report products derived from TED by private-sector firms, in addition to a demand for more detailed TED compilations and analyses to serve the needs of drug developers.

Conditional Approval

TED would make public a vast amount of both clinical trial data and observational data about new drug effectiveness before and during Phase III testing. Some drugs would show strikingly effective treatment results compared to available FDA-approved drugs. In these situations, many knowledgeable doctors may object to enrolling their patients in Phase III randomized control trials on the ethical grounds of not wanting to subject their patients to the risk of receiving an inferior drug or a useless placebo.

As previously noted, because it has a monopoly over drug access decisions, the FDA can currently ignore this ethical lapse and insist on more extensive testing. Dual Tracking takes that monopoly power away by allowing patients and their doctors to go around the FDA if they believe the Free To Choose Track offers a superior risk/reward opportunity.

In the new environment created by Dual Tracking, the formerly invisible costs of suffering and deaths due to delayed access to new drugs would become much more visible. Heightened public awareness of the opportunity costs would make things increasingly uncomfortable for the FDA. Contributing to this pressure would be the lack of insurance coverage for the new drugs that are in high demand on the Free To Choose Track when they appear to be delivering significant health improvements. Most private health insurance contracts cover only FDA-approved drugs. So lack of FDA approval could keep people with less financial means from obtaining the life-improving or life-saving drugs accessible on the Free To Choose Track. This is not a situation Americans would want and we would pressure the FDA to get more engaged with the needs of all of today's patients.

One way to help the FDA respond to public pressure to approve promising new drugs before Phase III trials are complete is for the Free To Choose Medicine Act to allow the FDA to grant *conditional approval* for a new drug based on a combination of results from clinical trials and Free To Choose Track use. To maintain conditional approval, the developer would have to agree to complete Phase III trials and obtain conventional FDA approval within a reasonable amount of time.

Instances of strikingly positive treatment outcomes for Free To Choose Track drugs would discourage some patients from enrolling in Phase III RCTs, where they might get a placebo or an inferior drug. This "problem" would not be caused by the proposed Dual Track system. Rather, it would be evidence that a large number of consumer-patients are making a voluntary choice of the medical treatment perceived to be in their best interest.

The proper response from the FDA would be to develop innovative Phase III methods giving top priority to the needs of today's patients and avoiding unethical RCTs.[7] It is worth repeating that, if patients and doctors are genuinely uncertain about the effectiveness of a new drug compared to an FDA-approved drug, the Dual Track system would not hamper enrollment in clinical trials that use both drugs.

Drug Developer Incentives

Consider a new drug that has successfully passed the Phase I safety trial and has reached the midpoint of its Phase II testing, thus providing a threshold level of treatment data for TED. The drug developer elects to put the drug on the Free To Choose Track. Legislation requires continuation of Phase II and III clinical testing in hopes of securing conventional FDA approval. Now some patients find the new drug's risk/reward profile to be appealing and begin to use the drug, and their results are reported on TED.

When data for a new drug suggest breakthrough potential for raising the standard of care, a large number of patients would elect the Free To Choose Track, many more than participate in clinical trials. This much-larger patient population could produce compelling observational data to support an FDA conditional approval, which would be of great commercial value to the company.

Revenues from the initial sale of the drug would be especially beneficial for smaller drug developers with high scientific skill but limited financial resources. Keep in mind that the developer would be motivated to charge a reasonable price in order to increase the number of early users. In addition, possible competition from other Free To Choose drugs would work to benefit patients as well.

Competition from the Free To Choose Track would eventually compel the FDA to streamline its testing requirements, which would significantly reduce the cost of clinical trials and thereby reduce the average cost of getting an approved drug to market. Higher levels of innovation in a competitive (non-regulated) industry would deliver more value to consumers.

For a sense of what is possible, note how today's personal computers deliver vastly greater performance compared to similarly priced early PCs. Dual Tracking would greatly elevate the level of competition by putting a premium on a company's ability to demonstrate scientific skill in delivering breakthrough drugs, as opposed to having deep pockets and high skill in navigating the FDA's bureaucracy.

Developers especially want fast-paced learning about how their drugs work for a variety of patients. Unexpected outcomes, both positive and negative, could greatly aid in clinical trial design for Phase III. If a drug shows disappointing effectiveness or serious adverse side effects when used by a substantial number of Free To Choose Track volunteers, the developer could make an early and appropriate decision to cancel both ongoing clinical trials and planned future trials. This would enable the developer's resources to more quickly be reallocated to more promising drugs.

Public knowledge of Free To Choose Track treatment results is complementary to the trend toward personalized medicine. Treatment results would help identify subsets of patients who achieve much better or worse outcomes than expected and generate hypotheses as to why this is so. As this information is continually updated and communicated via TED, patients and doctors would gain access to a knowledge base that becomes ever-more reliable over time. On the one hand, a developer might, all else equal, want to keep this type of information confidential.[8] On the other hand, a developer benefits as more doctors apply their problem-solving skills and knowledge of their patients in using the developer's drug.

TED would be a public good benefiting both today's and tomorrow's patients. TED would provide uniquely valuable data for substantially improving the R&D efforts of drug developers in general. In particular, large pharmaceutical companies typically have high-powered information technology capabilities ideally suited to exploit the treasure trove of data heretofore unavailable to any one firm.

Note that the results for the average of all patients in a drug's Phase III testing may not clear the FDA's statistical bar for approval. However, especially positive results may have been demonstrated for a subset of patients. To continue to strive for FDA approval, the developer would then be faced with the additional high cost of undertaking a new, redesigned Phase III trial to demonstrate efficacy for the subset of patients. In this situation, the Free To Choose Track would provide a win/win for the developer and the patients. Patients achieving positive results could continue to purchase the drug, and the revenues would help finance the developer's costs of having to run another clinical trial.

Gaining Support from the Pharmaceutical Industry

In my view, Free To Choose Medicine would be extraordinarily positive for both patients and the pharmaceutical industry.

It is an underappreciated fact that, over the long term, firms that do exceptionally well for their customers also do exceptionally well for their shareholders.[9] This simple fact underscores the opportunity for Dual Tracking to turbocharge R&D, accelerate the pace of development for new drugs that substantially improve the standard of care, increase firms' revenues sooner, and compel the FDA to streamline its regulatory load, leading to lower prescription drug prices for consumers—all the while earning the respect of consumers who today may feel cheated by drug companies charging sky-high prices for prescription drugs.

Does the pharmaceutical industry have another approach that could deliver such high value to both consumers and shareholders? I have not heard of any.

The industry does a lot of planning in the hope of avoiding further government price controls. More stringent price controls would dramatically reduce investments in new drugs, a terrible tragedy for future patients.

Price controls also would reduce company profits and common stock prices, harming shareholders. Big R&D successes would no longer bring big investment successes. Stock prices would drop to reflect the new reality that a "pure play" pharmaceutical company's stock has the substantial downside risk of drug development failures and the limited upside of a regulated utility stock. Pharmaceutical companies would have every incentive to reallocate their resources to business opportunities other than drug development R&D.

A preview of what comprehensive price controls would do to the pharmaceutical industry is offered by Sidney Taurel, former chairman and chief executive officer of Eli Lilly and Company:

> Those most vulnerable in a price-controlled future would logically be those that, today, are most committed to innovation. The biotech industry, in particular, would see terrible attrition. It's no coincidence that 70 percent of the world's biotech capability is located in the United States.
>
> ... [R]eaction to the threat of price controls, this flight from innovation, has happened before in the United States—twice, in fact. In the 1960s, in the aftermath of the notorious Kefauver hearings, we saw pharmaceutical companies rapidly diversifying into all sorts of business lines—agricultural chemicals, animal health products, cosmetics, medical devices, and diagnostics. That's how Lilly came to be, for a number of years, the owner of Elizabeth Arden cosmetics.
>
> The same thing happened in the early 1990s in reaction to the Clinton administration's proposed healthcare reforms, which many thought would

end market pricing in U.S. healthcare. There was a very rapid response within the industry. ... Industry investments in research had been increasing at more than 10 percent per year. All at once that rate fell to under 3 percent per year.

...We need to understand, once and for all, that innovation is not the problem. It is the solution.[10]

An Evolutionary Path for the FDA

Dual Tracking offers drug developers a way to bring new drugs to market faster and to learn faster by collecting more data on patient outcomes sooner. Dual Tracking offers patients and doctors choices not otherwise available, which can lead to improved health. Only highly risk-averse regulators and politicians who refuse to apply a systems mindset to the role of the FDA stand in the way. Yet, there are reasons for the FDA to elect an evolutionary path that recognizes the advantages of freedom of choice.

As previously discussed, regulators at the FDA don't want to be blamed for any injuries or deaths that occur on their watch and are perceived to be preventable. With Dual Tracking, the responsibility for access to new drugs is shifted to patients and doctors and away from the FDA as a guarantor of safe and effective drugs. Expanded choice brings with it the responsibility for patients to work with their doctors to make informed decisions about new drugs whose up-to-date treatment results are publicly available on TED. Those who do not want to accept this responsibility and opportunity would stay with using drugs that have earned the FDA's conventional approval.

Finally, as previously discussed, in a Dual Track environment there should be significant public pressure to help patients obtain insurance coverage for exceptionally promising drugs on the Free To Choose Track. The FDA could address this concern by granting conditional approval for drugs with compelling data suggesting substantial patient benefit. That is consistent with insurance companies' coverage for health treatments with demonstrated patient benefit. In these instances, the FDA would be a hero to organizations like the Abigail Alliance that strive mightily to bring potentially life-saving drugs to suffering patients.

This new environment might not be appreciated by those FDA officials who are diehard supporters of randomized control trials. But it could appeal to more forward-looking FDA officials who understand the importance of giving top priority to today's patients and who are aware of the accelerating trend in both personalized medicine and patient use of the Internet to gain knowledge to help guide their medical treatment.

Choice and Off-Label Drug Use

There already exists a segment of the medical marketplace where consumer choice is much less restricted than in the case of access to new drugs. Both sides of this debate should evaluate the results of the current environment of off-label drug use in which doctors can write prescriptions for drugs to be used in ways for which they are not approved by the FDA.

In this environment, doctors help their patients by participating in a shared knowledge base of treatment results for off-label drug use. Experiments abound and learning is fast-paced – quite the opposite of the FDA's clinical trial environment. Private-sector organizations provide doctors with up-to-date information on off-label drug treatment results. Doctors are especially pleased with this system because their patients are better off from greatly expanded choices. A leading researcher in the treatment of breast cancer noted, "If I had to use drugs for their approved uses only, half my patients would be dead."[11]

Off-label prescribing is a threat to the FDA and, to no surprise, in the past the FDA has tried to throw a regulatory blanket over this unregulated system. In a worst-case scenario the FDA would require clinical trials and approvals for new uses of approved drugs. Already, the FDA has gotten tougher on the information that drug manufacturers can disseminate, even disallowing relevant medical journal articles from being distributed to physicians. Monopolists always have in their cross-hairs for elimination any alternative system that might demonstrate a better way to serve consumers.

Off-label drug use is a window into an environment where things happen to best serve existing patients. We can observe how patients benefit from a continual stream of experiments by doctors who know a great deal about the unique medical conditions of each patient they are treating. In this world, it is common for a drug to be discovered to work surprisingly well for certain types of patients. What is at work here is observational data from an expanding variety of medical situations that indicates how very useful Dual Tracking and TED would be.

Alex Tabarrok, an economics professor at George Mason University, completed a study of off-label drug use in 2000. He reported:

I find that the largely unregulated system of off-label prescribing has large benefits and few costs. Off-label prescribing speeds medical innovations to patients, it increases the number of drugs available to doctors, and it lowers the costs of medical innovation. Consistent with these benefits, off-label prescribing is widespread and common in the United States today. The largely unregulated system of off-label prescribing is thus working well and should be extended ... [A]n analysis of off-label prescribing strongly suggests that the FDA's authority over new drugs, particularly the requirement that new drugs be tested for efficacy, appears to be detrimental to the health and welfare of U.S. health consumers and thus should be ended.[12]

The Thalidomide Baby Question

Any proposal to bypass the FDA has to face the "thalidomide baby question." Would Dual Tracking make us more susceptible to a safety crisis like the infamous thalidomide baby episode that led to the 1962 legislation that greatly expanded the FDA's testing of new drugs? The answer is "No."

Thalidomide was developed as a sedative (sleeping pill) in Germany in the late 1950s. Approval to market it in the U.S. was delayed by the FDA due to concerns about safety. The FDA's demand for more-rigorous safety evidence was certainly warranted as it soon became apparent that many pregnant women who used the drug to alleviate morning sickness subsequently gave birth to babies with deformed limbs. Pictures of babies with truncated limbs that resembled flippers created a rallying call for tighter government testing of new drugs.

Some might immediately object to Dual Tracking because it suggests a reduction of FDA power that could lead to safety crises similar to the thalidomide episode. However, when it was first introduced, thalidomide was expected to be used primarily to relieve the symptoms of insomnia, coughs, colds, and headaches. It was not until after the product was introduced commercially that it was prescribed to treat morning sickness. Consequently, there is no convincing reason to believe the tragic birth defects that resulted from the drug's use by pregnant women would have been discovered through RCTs prior to approval even if the manufacturer had been required to conduct more stringent clinical testing. Pregnant women would not have been participants in RCTs.

Would Dual Tracking lead to safety crises such as this? No. First, today's technological advancements make preclinical testing by drug developers for safety and the FDA's Phase I safety trial an order of magnitude better than tests used during the 1960s. Incidentally, even 1960s test technology produced enough red flags to cause the FDA to delay thalidomide approval in spite of enormous pressure from the U.S. firm, Richardson-Merrell, to expedite marketing approval.[13] Today's technology provides better sharing of information through the Internet, better computer modeling of a drug's effects in humans, better understanding of the mechanisms of the action of chemicals and proteins in the human body, better understanding of human metabolism and the action of metabolic byproducts of drugs, and a better understanding of the shortcomings associated with animal testing.

Let's consider a hypothetical new drug that has as-yet-undetected terrible side effects and has entered Phase II clinical testing. Recall that, under the proposed Dual Track system, doctors cannot recommend, and patients cannot purchase, a new drug until it has completed the initial half of Phase II testing and the developer elects to put the drug on the Free To Choose Track. Participating doctors would be required to report side effects in a timely fashion to the Tradeoff Evaluation Database. And TED would quickly communicate reports of adverse side effects during this Phase II testing. Such real-time Internet updating of treatment results obviously was unavailable in the late 1950s and early 1960s.

Further, let's assume that only the patients with an unusual health attribute exhibit the serious side effect. If they were enrolled in Phase II or III testing, TED would communicate any adverse side effects to doctors who were considering the new drug. However, the homogeneity of patient enrollment in Phase II and III could easily exclude those with the unusual attribute. But since patients who use the Free To Choose Track would more likely constitute a representative cross-section of the broader, heterogeneous general population, the effect should be revealed. In this situation, it is much more likely that Free To Choose patients – who do not need to meet the strict patient enrollment criteria for clinical trials – would include those who subsequently suffer the serious side effect, so such side effects would be more likely to be detected earlier. The conclusion is that voluntary expanded use by Free To Choose patients would work to the benefit of those who use only approved drugs.

The Free To Choose Track enables patients and their doctors to decide if and when a non-approved new drug is in their best interests to purchase and use. They can elect to wait until essentially all of Phase III results are posted on TED plus up-to-date results from the Free To Choose Track.

They can elect to avoid all unapproved drugs for less-than-life-threatening illnesses, such as insomnia or allergies.

The essential point, as stated by Daniel Klein and Alex Tabarrok, is:

> A drug stamped "safe" by the FDA is usually not safe for every particular case or individual, and a drug not so stamped is, nonetheless, safe for many particular cases and individuals. ... But the relevant benchmark is not a state of perfect health. What really matters is whether taking the drug is *safer* than not taking the drug. The people intimately concerned in the situation and intimately informed ... should make this determination. (italics in the original)[14]

Today, thalidomide is FDA-approved for the treatment of leprosy and multiple myeloma, and it is being studied for treating inflammatory diseases, HIV-related ulcers, and cancer. This reaffirms that treating safety as an absolute condition, divorced from the context of a particular disease and a patient's unique circumstances, is counterproductive.

Conclusion

Freedom of choice via Dual Tracking would benefit today's patients while simultaneously providing an enormously rich database to improve current treatment decisions and generate hypotheses for drug companies that would yield future innovations. Casting the issue as an either/or proposition – help today's patients or help future patients – is a false choice.

The delivery of better drugs over the long term depends on a system that not only evaluates a particular new drug that is in clinical trials, but also expedites the learning that leads to better drugs in the future. To that end, observational data on TED could play an important role in expediting experimentation and learning, offering profoundly important improvements for the performance of the total drugs-to-patients system.[15]

Voluntary decisions by consumers within a competitive system provide continuous feedback as to what they value and what works for them. Consider a company with high hopes that its new drug being tested will deliver an improved standard of care. If use on the Free To Choose Track were to produce particularly positive results, more consumers would buy the product and more data would become available on TED, which would lead to better-informed decisions. Conversely, use would plummet if initial use of a new drug produced negative results.

The Dual Track system is dynamic and enables patients and doctors to adapt over time in response to how new drugs perform, all the while providing data that are useful for generating hypotheses concerning drug effectiveness for subsets of patients and for further evaluating those hypotheses as use increases. This ability to adapt to changing conditions is a huge advantage as we enter an era of unprecedented advances in medical technology.

Chapter 5
How to Change the System

For what avail the plough or sail, or land or life, if freedom fail?

Ralph Waldo Emerson

Prior chapters have introduced the systems mindset that sheds light on why the continual demands for expanded FDA testing are at cross-purposes with the rightful goal of better drugs, sooner, at lower cost. Too many people suffer unnecessary pain and die prematurely because the FDA slows the approval process and increases the cost of new drugs.

We now know there is a solution. A Free To Choose Medicine Act will create a Dual Track system that enables patients and their doctors to choose faster access to promising new drugs. Their decisions will be informed by TED (a Tradeoff Evaluation Database) filled with real-time data from clinical trials as well as observational data provided by doctors and patients using drugs outside clinical trials.

Now comes the hard part. How to change the system? Good ideas don't automatically transform themselves into good legislation. How do we persuade Congress to pass, and the president to sign, a Free To Choose Medicine Act? Let's begin by envisioning what success would look like.

Envisioning Success

What do I mean by "free to choose?" I consider personal freedom to be the power to act to achieve a purpose in accordance with informed choice, while not injuring others. For such freedom to thrive, a society's culture must value the feedback observable in the consequences of actions taken so that knowledge improves over time, thereby creating new opportunities for informed choices.

A preference for consumer choice over bureaucratic control is consistent with this view of freedom. But the proposal in this book for breaking the FDA's monopoly is not based solely on an argument for more freedom and less government as a matter of principle. While of utmost importance, freedom is only one component of a larger system.

We need the drugs-to-patients system to quickly adapt to a changing environment. A reasonable forecast is that the future will bring an accelerated pace of medical innovation, coupled to the widespread advancement of personalized medicine. Diagnostic testing will match patients according to their genetic makeup with drugs that are much more likely to work and to have fewer adverse side effects. In this environment, early access becomes more and more beneficial over time. Dual Tracking would accommodate early access and dramatically speed up the delivery of medical advancements.

With the Free To Choose Track, a new drug showing strongly positive results would lead to a surge in use by patients with diverse characteristics that more accurately reflect the general patient population of drug users than do the patients enrolled in FDA's randomized controlled trials. Consequently, upon receiving FDA approval, drugs would have a *more reliable safety profile* if they were used by patients on the Free To Choose Track. Consumers who choose to use only approved drugs would benefit from the voluntary decisions of those willing to accept more risk in exchange for early access.

Dual Tracking would most likely lead to substantially lower prescription drug prices. Firms invest with plans for achieving a satisfactory return on investment (ROI) commensurate with the risk. The longer it takes before drug revenues are received and the higher the expenditures for clinical testing, the lower the ROI, all else unchanged. It should not be shocking that a decade-long clinical testing and approval process with a tab of a billion dollars leads to very high prescription drug prices set by drug companies striving to achieve a satisfactory ROI. Lower drug prices can be achieved without government control of prices in two ways: (1) change the environment so that drug companies, all else equal, can achieve the same level of ROI with lower prescription drug prices and (2) promote greater competition among drug companies. With Dual Tracking, both are achieved.

Drug development firms would receive revenue sooner from the sale of drugs through the Free To Choose Track, especially if conditional approval is obtained. In addition, information on TED about Free To Choose drugs would lead to increased efficiency of the development part of firms' research and development outlays; i.e., faster and more accurate decisions about which new drug programs to shut down and which to accelerate. The entire design of Dual Tracking spurs innovation and competition not only for drug companies, but also for the FDA.

Perhaps the biggest reduction in prescription drug prices would follow from the plain evidence of how well patients do when they circumvent the FDA regulatory process. Such feedback would be expected to compel the FDA to radically streamline its testing process with a concomitant reduction in regulatory costs for drug developers. Allowing the FDA to give conditional approval to the most promising new drugs would enable patients (consumers) to gain insurance coverage for drugs available from the Free To Choose Track. The FDA could use that to respond positively to new evidence from TED and the related pressure from patients and their doctors. If the FDA doesn't want to take on the analytical challenge of working with TED's observational data, it could contract out to the private sector the analysis of TED data (both clinical trial use and Free To Choose use) as well as the determination of when conditional approval is warranted.

To sum it all up, Dual Tracking would put us on a competitive path to lower prescription drug prices while advancing innovation – exactly opposite of a price control path to lower drug prices that some health care reform advocates are pushing. Their option would seriously reduce long-term innovation.

Passage of a Free To Choose Medicine Act would be a defining moment for America – a directional change from today's trend of increasing litigation and regulation and a stake in the ground that control of medical decisions belongs, first and foremost, with individual patients and doctors, and not the government.

Overcoming Obstacles – Yes We Can

Drug companies might initially hesitate to put a new drug on the Free To Choose Track in fear the FDA would incorporate negative results from the Free To Choose Track in its approval decision, but ignore positive results. Forward-looking managements could overcome this concern if they conclude that their top priority is to transition to a different business model attuned to the Dual Track system. With such a system, shareholder interests are aligned with the goal of better drugs, sooner, at lower cost.

Another obstacle to overcome are trial lawyers and their lobbyists, who are sure to wage a colossal battle to remove any provision in legislation to grant immunity to those involved with the delivery of Free To Choose drugs. Philip Howard, founder of Common Good, a legal reform coalition, recently wrote,

> The growth of litigation and regulation has injected a paralyzing uncertainty into everyday choices. All around us are warnings and legal risks. The modern credo is not 'Yes We Can' but 'No You Can't. Most doctors say they wouldn't advise their children to go into medicine. ... Reviving the can-do spirit that made America great requires a legal overhaul of historic dimensions ... to affirmatively protect individual freedom in daily choices.[1]

Of course, society benefits from lawsuits that punish those who harm others through gross negligence and fraudulent behavior. Nevertheless, it is also true that excessive lawsuits have resulted in enormous and wasteful costs from the practice of defensive medicine and from skyrocketing medical malpractice insurance costs due to the misconduct of some members of the plaintiff's bar.

"Trial Lawyers, Inc." (see http://www.triallawyersinc.com) is a very big business and it will unleash a green river of political contributions to Washington directed at defeating a Free To Choose Medicine Act. Effective legislation, after all, would show Americans the benefits to be gained from the elimination of frivolous lawsuits and a return to common sense and personal responsibility by way of voluntary contracts.

Building a Reform Movement

How, then, do we build a reform movement for Free To Choose Medicine? We start by exposing the fundamental but faulty assumption that prevents the FDA, the pharmaceutical industry, and we Americans from coming together to support freedom of choice. That faulty assumption is that the FDA should be the guarantor of safe and effective drugs. In its place, we must recognize and become comfortable with the reality that drug use is, fundamentally, a tradeoff decision involving risk versus opportunity for health improvement.

To achieve Free To Choose Medicine, one early objective must be to spread the messages presented in this book, as widely as possible, in order to gain the public support that is a prerequisite to gaining political attention and eventual action in Washington. Some ideas for spreading the message appear later in this chapter.

Another early objective is to get support and eventual participation from at least some firms in the developmental drug business. Perhaps small biotech companies, believing their new drugs truly represent a breakthrough in patient care, will be the initial users of the Free To Choose Track. This use could bring a sea change in the competitive landscape to the benefit of patients. Other drug companies would then be forced to respond to this new competition and they, too, might adopt a fast-track approach.

Advocacy groups that typically find themselves on the political left or political right ought to see the value in working to pass a Free To Choose Medicine Act. Advocacy groups on both sides made huge investments in the recent health care reform debate, and they seem to have been left empty-handed. Why not endorse a realistic plan that would be hugely popular with their members, would genuinely lower health care costs, and would bring heightened competition to drug companies?

Groups that lean to the right should be quick to embrace Free To Choose Medicine. They have been criticized for not having their own positive agenda for health care reform. Better drugs, sooner, at lower cost fills that void.

Business groups from the U.S. Chamber of Commerce to the smallest city chamber of commerce ought to take up the call for Free To Choose Medicine in order to achieve better health outcomes from health insurance expenditures. Innovative drugs have a proven record of reducing health care costs by making surgery and hospitalization less necessary. Faster access to new drugs is one way to "bend the curve" of health care spending downward without the long-term deleterious effects of price controls.

This is quite a line-up of powerful potential allies. It is not unrealistic to imagine some or all of these groups joining a coalition for Free To Choose Medicine. They just need to be informed, persuaded, and encouraged to act.

What You Can Do Right Now

Here is a list of seven actions you can take that, in the aggregate, can be far more important than anything the big organizations mentioned above might do.

First, write to your elected representatives in Washington and tell them you support legislation giving people the right to use drugs that are still in advanced clinical testing. And then continue to write once every month until the legislation is passed. Members of Congress do pay attention to the volume of letters they receive from their constituents. Write ... and then keep writing!

Second, write a letter to the editor of your local newspaper explaining how millions of people are suffering unnecessarily, and thousands die every year, because of our flawed system of drug testing. Call on other readers to stand up for the rights of the sick and dying in their community. Urge them to write to their elected officials too.

Third, call or write to the reporters in the newspapers or magazines you read who cover health care issues, and express your support for the reform plan set forth in this book. Question them about the "invisible graveyard" of deaths caused by regulatory delay. Confront them when they exploit the small number of deaths due to approved drugs, and point out how this simply plays into the hands of the regulators who are most responsible for needless suffering and deaths.

Fourth, talk to doctors and other health care professionals in your community and recruit them to support your cause. Urge them to read this book and the literature available from patient advocacy groups concerned with the right to choose medical treatment. Get them on our side, or at least keep them from blindly opposing consumer choice.

Fifth, learn more about the Abigail Alliance and other patient advocacy groups and encourage them to support the Free To Choose Medicine Act.

Sixth, persuade the civic and business groups of which you are a member to take up this cause. Your local chamber of commerce, Rotary Club, senior organizations, and any number of other clubs and associations should be actively involved in this issue. After all, it affects the health and well-being of every member and their families.

Seventh, regularly check the progress of the Free To Choose Medicine movement at the website, http://www.FreeToChooseMedicine.com. This is the "go to" place for up-to-date information, including current opportunities to participate in this new movement.

If you are a doctor, nurse, or other provider in the health care system, you can be especially influential in the movement for Free To Choose Medicine. Talk to your patients about the problem of denied access to new drugs and what they can do to pressure Congress for reform. Get your clinic, hospital, or practice group to show support for Free To Choose Medicine.

If you are an entrepreneur or venture capitalist, consider the investment opportunities that Free To Choose Medicine would create and support the legislation described. Congress is more likely to act if investors indicate they see large-scale innovation opportunities from new legislation.

Finally, if you are a philanthropist, consider supporting the think tanks where many of the seminal thinkers (mentioned in the Preface) work and other think tanks that support consumer choice for health care. Prominent among them are American Enterprise Institute, Competitive Enterprise Institute, Eudoxa, Galen Institute, Heartland Institute, Hoover Institution, Independent Institute, Manhattan Institute, Medicine & Liberty, Mercatus Center, Pacific Research Institute, and Reason Foundation. Ask them to earmark your support for this issue.

Conclusion

I urge you to join a reform movement devoted to getting faster access to promising new drugs, especially for patients enduring chronic pain or the prospect of terminal illness. These patients are up against one of the largest and most powerful government bureaucracies in the world. Because many of them are sick or even dying, they often lack the energy and/or resources to carry on the battle themselves.

Based on the mood of the country as I write this book in 2010, this new reform movement could turn out to be one of the most popular and vocal movements of our times. The victims are many and their pain and suffering is very real. Scientific and medical discoveries are creating a huge wave of new drugs with genuine promise for new standards of care in managing pain and disease while adding productive years to our lifetimes. The Internet makes it possible for enormous amounts of real-time data on drug effects to be shared by patients, doctors, pharmaceutical companies, and regulators. Old regulations passed before such data were widely available are obviously archaic and need to be changed.

What's missing from this picture? You.

Make your voice heard. A phone call to your elected officials would really make a difference. Talk to your neighbors; join coalitions and organizations that are dedicated to this vital cause. For all the victims of the FDA's deadly overcaution, for your future and your family and friends, stand up and be counted. We can stop the suffering and unnecessary deaths.

It really is in your hands. One person at a time, we can make the difference.

Notes

Chapter 1

1. Quoted in Jerome Groopman, "The Right To A Trial," *New Yorker*, December 18, 2006.

2. See John E. Calfee, "Patient Power," *Weekly Standard*, May 8, 2006.

3. Quoted from Steven Walker, "Decelerated Approval" (paper presented to the Oncologic Drugs Advisory Committee, November 8, 2005), www.abigail-alliance.org.

4. Supra note 2.

5. See National Consumers League, "Public Attitudes towards Risk, Regulation, and Patient Voices in the Treatment of Chronic, Debilitating Conditions," March 2006. The survey margin of error was +/- 3 percentage points.

6. See Tomas J. Philipson and Anupam B. Jena, "Who Benefits From New Medical Technologies? Estimates of Consumer and Producer Surpluses for HIV/AIDS Drugs," *Forum for Health Economics and Policy* 9, no. 2 (2006).

7. See John E. Calfee, "The Golden Age of Medical Innovation," *The American*, March/April 2007; and John E. Calfee, "The Indispensable Industry," *The American*, May/June 2008.

8. See Eric C. Sun et al., "An Economic Evaluation of the War on Cancer," National Bureau of Economic Research, *Working Paper* #15574, December 2009.

9. Based on Phase III clinical trial data summarized at http://www.gene.com/gene/products/information/tgr/lucentis/ (accessed 24 January 2010).

10. See Scott Gottlieb, "Stem Cells and the Truth about Medical Innovation," *The Wall Street Journal*, March 13, 2009.

Chapter 2

1. For more on systems thinking, see "A Systems Mindset," Chapter 1 in Bartley J. Madden, *Wealth Creation: A Systems Mindset for Building and Investing in Businesses for the Long Term* (Hoboken, NJ: John Wiley & Sons, Inc., 2010), 1-17.

2. Ibid., Chapter 2, "The Wealth Creation System," 19-33; and Chapter 3, "The Ideal Free-Market System," 35-43.

3. William J. Baumol, *The Free-Market Innovation Machine: Analyzing the Growth Miracle of Capitalism* (Princeton, NJ: Princeton University Press, 2002), viii-ix.

4. See Stephen Moore, "Push Ethanol Off the Dole," July 10, 1997, www.cato.org. In theory, ethanol subsidies could be justified as a means to reduce dependence on foreign oil in order to deny totalitarian regimes oil revenues that may finance global terrorism.

5. "What Price Socialism? An Economy without Information," Chapter 3 in Scott Shane, *Dismantling Utopia: How Information Ended The Soviet Union* (Chicago, IL: Ivan R. Dee, 1994), 75-98.

6. Joseph A. DiMasi, Ronald W. Hansen, and Henry G. Grabowski, "The price of innovation: new estimates of drug development costs," *Journal of Health Economics* 22 (2003), 151-185.

7. Henry I. Miller, *To America's Health: A Proposal to Reform the Food and Drug Administration* (Stanford, CA: Hoover Institution Press, 2000), 41-42.

8. See Sam Kazman, "Deadly Overcaution: FDA's Drug Approval Process," *Journal of Regulation and Social Costs* 1, no. 1 (September 1990), 41.

9. The website www.fdareview.org is a project of the Independent Institute. It contains an excellent and comprehensive analysis of the FDA. Key economic issues are also addressed in Sam Peltzman, *Regulation of Pharmaceutical Innovation: The 1962 Amendments* (Washington, DC: American Enterprise Institute, 1974); Robert Higgs, "Banning a Risky Product Cannot Improve Any Consumer's Welfare (Properly Understood), with Applications to FDA Testing Requirements," *Review of Austrian Economics* 7, no. 2 (1994), 3-20; Gary S. Becker, "Get the FDA Out of the Way, and Drug Prices Will Drop," *Business Week*, September 16, 2002, 16; Gary S. Becker, "Big Ideas: Patient Rights," *Milken Institute Review*, Second Quarter 2004, 93-94; and Jerome Arnett, Jr. and Gregory Conko, "FDA's Bad Medicine," Competitive Enterprise Institute, August 13, 2008.

10. Supra note 7, Chapter 3, "Reforming the Current System," 35-48.

11. See Mark Thornton, "The Clinical Trial," *The Wall Street Journal*, February 12, 2007, A14.

12. FDA Subcommittee on Science and Technology, *Science and Mission at Risk*, prepared for FDA Science Board, November 2007, 3, 5.

Chapter 3

1. Austin Bradford Hill, *Statistical Methods in Clinical and Preventive Medicine* (London: E&S Livingstone Ltd., 1962), Chapter 4.

2. See Richard A. Epstein, *Overdose: How Excessive Government Regulation Stifles Pharmaceutical Innovation* (New Haven, CT: Yale University Press, 2006).

3. See http://www.annals.org/content/127/6/429.full.

4. See John E. Calfee, "Patient Power," *Weekly Standard*, May 8, 2006.

5. Quoted from Steven Walker, "Decelerated Approval" (paper presented to the Oncologic Drugs Advisory Committee, November 8, 2005), www.abigail-alliance.org.

6. As noted on www.abigail-alliance.org (accessed November 11, 2009).

7. A particularly illuminating analysis of equipoise is contained in Franklin G. Miller and Howard Brody, "A Critique of Clinical Equipoise: Therapeutic Misconception in the Ethics of Clinical Trials," *Hastings Center Report* 33, no. 3 (2003), 19-28.

8. Spyros Retsas, "Treatment at Random: The Ultimate Science or the Betrayal of Hippocrates?" *Journal of Clinical Oncology* 24 (December 15, 2004), 5005-8.

9. Scott H. Donaldson et al.,"Mucus Clearance and Lung Function in Cystic Fibrosis with Hypertonic Saline," *New England Journal of Medicine* 354, no. 3 (January 19, 2006), 241-250; and Mark R. Elkins et al., "A Controlled Trial of Long-Term Inhaled Hypertonic Saline in Patients with Cystic Fibrosis," *New England Journal of Medicine* 354, no. 3 (January 19, 2006), 229-40.

Chapter 4

1. The following publications by Bartley J. Madden helped shape the ideas in this chapter: "Breaking the FDA Monopoly," *Regulation*, Summer 2004, 64-6; "A Clinical Trial for the Food and Drug Administration's Clinical Trial Process," *Cancer, Biotherapy & Radiopharmaceuticals* 20, no 6 (2005), 569-78; *More*

Choices, Better Health: Free to Choose Experimental Drugs (Chicago, IL: The Heartland Institute, 2007); and "A dual track system to give more-rapid access to new drugs: Applying a systems mindset to the US food and drug administration (FDA)," *Medical Hypotheses* 72 (2009), 116-20.

2. For a discussion of this legal issue, see Richard A. Epstein, *Overdose: How Excessive Government Regulation Stifles Pharmaceutical Innovation* (New Haven, CT: Yale University Press, 2006).

3. *Restatement (Third) of Torts: Products Liability* §18, cmt. a (1998).

4. Richard A. Epstein, *Overdose: How Excessive Government Regulation Stifles Pharmaceutical Innovation* (New Haven, CT: Yale University Press, 2006), 188; Chapters 16, 17, and 18 provide a useful overview of drug liability.

5. For an insightful analysis of ways to speed up the delivery of effective cancer therapeutics, see Philip A. Schein and Barbara Scheffler, "Barriers to Efficient Development of Cancer Therapeutics," *Clinical Cancer Research* 12, no. 11 (June 1, 2006), 3243-48.

6. Alexander T. Tabarrok, "Bringing the Consumer Revolution to the FDA," Independent Institute, *Commentary*, April 25, 2005.

7. "Types of Randomized Controlled Trials," Chapter 2 in Alejandro R. Jadad and Murray W. Enkin, *Randomized Controlled Trials* (Malden, MA: Blackwell Publishing, 2007, 2d edition), 12-28.

8. See Aaron S. Kesselhelm and Michelle M. Mello, "Confidentiality Laws And Secrecy In Medical Research: Improving Public Access To Data On Drug Safety," *Health Affairs* 26, no. 2 (2007), 483-91.

9. "The Competitive Life-Cycle View of the Firm," Chapter 4 in Bartley J. Madden, *Wealth Creation: A Systems Mindset for Building and Investing in Businesses for the Long Term* (Hoboken, NJ: John Wiley & Sons, Inc., 2010), 45-77.

10. Sidney Taurel, "The Campaign Against Innovation," in *Ethics and the Pharmaceutical Industry*, ed. Michael A. Santaro and Thomas M. Gorrie (Cambridge, MA: Cambridge University Press, 2005), 326-35.

11. Dr. Larry Norton quoted in Robert M. Goldberg, "Breaking Up the FDA's Medical Information Monopoly," *Regulation* 18, no. 2 (1995), 40-52.

12. Alexander T. Tabarrok, "Assessing the FDA via the Anomaly of Off-Label Drug Prescribing," *Independent Review*, Summer 2000, 25-53.

13. For a comprehensive analysis of the history of thalidomide, see Rock Brynner and Trent Stephens, *Dark Remedy: The Impact of Thalidomide and its Revival as a Vital Medicine* (New York, NY: Basic Books, 2001).

14. Quote is from the authors of www.FDAReview.org, "Some Remarks about 'Safety'" (accessed 1 January 2010.).

15. Ways to coordinate a Free To Choose Track with the conventional FDA clinical trial track or different ways to operate TED could be evaluated in a very low-cost manner via laboratory experiments (see http://www.ifreeweb.org). An important first step has already been taken with Daniel Houser et al., "Dual Track: A Laboratory Analysis of a Market Based Complement to the FDA," George Mason University, *Working Paper*, October 2009.

Chapter 5

1. Philip K. Howard, "How Modern Law Makes Us Powerless," *The Wall Street Journal*, January 26, 2009, A15.

References

Adams, Christopher P. and Van V. Brantner. "Estimating the Cost of New Drug Development: Is It Really $802 Million?" *Health Affairs* 25 (2006): 420-28.

American Law Institute, *Restatement (Third) of Torts: Products Liability*, 1998.

Arnett, Jerome, Jr. and Gregory Conko. "FDA's Bad Medicine." Washington, DC: Competitive Enterprise Institute, August 13, 2008.

Baumol, William J. *The Free-Market Innovation Machine: Analyzing the Growth Miracle of Capitalism.* Princeton, NJ: Princeton University Press, 2002.

Becker, Gary S. "Get The FDA Out Of The Way, And Drug Prices Will Drop." *Business Week*, September 16, 2002, 16.

Becker, Gary S. "Big Ideas: Patient Rights." *Milken Institute Review*, Second Quarter 2004, 93-4.

Brynner, Rock and Trent Stephens. *Dark Remedy: The Impact of Thalidomide and its Revival as a Vital Medicine.* New York, NY: Basic Books, 2001.

Calfee, John E. "Patient Power." *Weekly Standard*, May 8, 2006.

Calfee, John E. "The Golden Age of Medical Innovation." *The American*, March/April 2007.

Calfee, John E. "The Indispensable Industry." *The American*, May/June 2008.

Dewey, John. *Human Nature and Conduct.* New York, NY: Modern Library, 1922.

DiMasi, Joseph A., Ronald W. Hansen, and Henry G. Grabowski. "The price of innovation: new estimates of drug development costs." *Journal of Health Economics* 22 (2003): 151-85.

Donaldson, Scott H. et al. "Mucus Clearance and Lung Function in Cystic Fibrosis with Hypertonic Saline." *New England Journal of Medicine* 354, no. 3 (January 19, 2006): 241-50.

Elkins, Mark R. et al. "A Controlled Trial of Long-Term Inhaled Hypertonic Saline in Patients with Cystic Fibrosis." *New England Journal of Medicine* 354, no. 3 (January 19, 2006): 229-40.

Epstein, Richard A. "Medical Malpractice, Imperfect information, and the Contractual Foundations for Medical Services." *Law and Contemporary Problems* 49, no. 2 (1986): 201-12.

Epstein, Richard A. *Overdose: How Excessive Government Regulation Stifles Pharmaceutical Innovation.* New Haven, CT: Yale University Press, 2006.

FDA Subcommittee on Science and Technology, *Science and Mission at Risk,* prepared for FDA Science Board, November 2007.

Friedman, Milton. *Capitalism and Freedom.* Chicago, IL: University of Chicago Press, 1962.

Goldberg, Robert M. "Breaking Up the FDA's Medical Information Monopoly." *Regulation* 18, no. 2 (1995): 40-52.

Gottlieb, Scott. "Stem Cells and the Truth about Medical Innovation." *The Wall Street Journal,* March 13, 2009.

Groopman, Jerome. "The Right To A Trial." *New Yorker,* December 18, 2006.

Houser, Daniel et al. "Dual Track: A Laboratory Analysis of a Market Based Complement to the FDA." George Mason University, *Working Paper,* 2009.

Higgs, Robert. "Banning a Risky Product Cannot Improve Any Consumer's Welfare (Properly Understood), with Applications to FDA Testing Requirements." *Review of Austrian Economics* 7, no. 2 (1994): 3-20.

Hill, Austin Bradford. *Statistical Methods in Clinical and Preventive Medicine.* London: E & S Livingstone Ltd., 1962.

Howard, Philip K. "How Modern Law Makes Us Powerless." *The Wall Street Journal,* January 26, 2009, A15.

Jadad, Alejandro R. and Murray W. Enkin. *Randomized Controlled Trials.* 2nd edition. Malden, MA: Blackwell Publishing, 2007.

Kazman, Sam. "Deadly Overcaution: FDA's Drug Approval Process." *Journal of Regulation and Social Costs* 1, no. 1 (September 1990): 35-54.

Kesselhelm, Aaron S. and Michelle M. Mello. "Confidentiality Laws And Secrecy In Medical Research: Improving Public Access To Data On Drug Safety." *Health Affairs* 26, no. 2 (2007): 483-91.

Madden, Bartley J. "Breaking the FDA Monopoly." *Regulation*, Summer 2004, 64-6.

Madden, Bartley J. "A Clinical Trial for the Food and Drug Administration's Clinical Trial Process." *Cancer Biotherapy & Radiopharmaceuticals* 20, no. 6 (2005), 569-78.

Madden, Bartley J. *More Choices, Better Health: Free to Choose Experimental Drugs*. Chicago, IL: Heartland Institute, 2007.

Madden, Bartley J. "A dual track system to give more-rapid access to new drugs: Applying a systems mindset to the US food and drug administration (FDA)." *Medical Hypotheses* 72 (2009): 116-20.

Madden, Bartley J. *Wealth Creation: A Systems Mindset for Building and Investing in Businesses for the Long Term*. Hoboken, NJ: John Wiley & Sons, Inc., 2010.

Miller, Franklin G. and Howard Brody. "A Critique of Clinical Equipoise: Therapeutic Misconception in the Ethics of Clinical Trials." *Hastings Center Report* 33, no. 3 (2003), 19-28.

Miller, Henry I. *To America's Health: A Proposal to Reform the Food and Drug Administration*. Stanford, CA: Hoover Institution Press, 2000.

Moore, Stephen. "Push Ethanol Off the Dole." www.cato.org, July 10, 1997.

National Consumers League. "Public Attitudes towards Risk, Regulation, and Patient Voices in the Treatment of Chronic, Debilitating Conditions." March 2006.

Peltzman, Sam. *Regulation of Pharmaceutical Innovation: The 1962 Amendments*. Washington, DC: American Enterprise Institute, 1974.

Peltzman, Sam. *Regulation and the Natural Progress of Opulence*. Washington, DC: American Enterprise Institute, 2005.

Philipson, Tomas J. and Anupam B. Jena. "Who Benefits From New Medical Technologies? Estimates of Consumer and Producer Surpluses for HIV/AIDS Drugs." *Forum for Health Economics and Policy* 9, no. 2 (2006).

Retsas, Spyros. "Treatment at Random: The Ultimate Science or the Betrayal of Hippocrates?" *Journal of Clinical Oncology* 22, no. 24 (December 15, 2004): 5005-8.

Schein, Philip A. and Barbara Scheffler. "Barriers to Efficient Development of Cancer Therapeutics." *Clinical Cancer Research* 12, no. 11 (June 1, 2006): 3243-8.

Scott, Shane. *Dismantling Utopia: How Information Ended The Soviet Union.* Chicago, IL: Ivan R. Dee, 1994.

Sun, Eric C. et al. "An Economic Evaluation of the War on Cancer." National Bureau of Economic Research, *Working Paper* #15574, December 2009.

Tabarrok, Alexander T. "Assessing the FDA via the Anomaly of Off-Label Drug Prescribing." *Independent Review*, Summer 2000, 25-53.

Tabarrok, Alexander T. "Bringing the Consumer Revolution to the FDA." Independent Institute, *Commentary*, April 25, 2005.

Taurel, Sidney. "The Campaign Against Innovation." In *Ethics and the Pharmaceutical Industry*, edited by Michael A. Santaro and Thomas M. Gorrie, 326-35. Cambridge, MA: Cambridge University Press, 2005.

Thornton, Mark. "The Clinical Trial." *The Wall Street Journal*, February 12, 2007, A14.

Walker, Steven. "Decelerated Approval." Paper presented to the Oncologic Drugs Advisory Committee, November 8, 2005. www.abigail-alliance.org.

Walker, Steven. "A Different 'Right to Life.'" *The Wall Street Journal*, January 11, 2008, A10.

Yeager, Leland B. "Is There A Bias Toward Overregulation?" in *Rights and Regulation: Ethical, Political, and Economic Issues*, edited by Tibor R. Machan and M. Bruce Johnson. San Francisco, CA: Pacific Institute for Public Policy Research, 1983.

About the Author

Bartley J. Madden is an independent researcher whose current focus is on market-based solutions to public policy issues (see www.LearningWhatWorks.com). His writing about the proposed Dual Track system to circumvent the FDA's monopoly on access to not-yet-approved drugs has appeared in *Regulation, Cancer Biotherapy & Radiopharmaceuticals*, and *Medical Hypotheses*, as well as a monograph titled *More Choices, Better Health* published by The Heartland Institute.

After receiving a BS in mechanical engineering, working as an engineer, and spending time in the Army, Madden earned an MBA at the University of California - Berkeley. In 1969 he co-founded Callard, Madden & Associates, where his research was instrumental in developing what is known as the CFROI (cash-flow-return-on-investment) valuation model, which is widely used by large money management firms today.

After managing portfolios for Harbor Capital Advisors for eight years, Madden joined HOLT Value Associates in the early 1990s, a firm created to extend the CFROI framework and provide consulting services to portfolio managers and corporate managers. HOLT was acquired by Credit Suisse in 2002, at which time Madden became a managing director of Credit Suisse/HOLT. He retired from Credit Suisse in late 2003.

His book, *Wealth Creation: A Systems Mindset for Building and Investing in Businesses for the Long Term*, was published in 2010.

About The Heartland Institute

The Heartland Institute is a nonprofit, nonpartisan research organization based in Chicago. Founded in 1984, it is devoted to discovering, developing, and promoting free-market solutions to social and economic problems.

The Heartland Institute contacts more elected officials, more often, than any other think tank in the United States. According to a telephone survey of 500 randomly selected state and local officials conducted by Victory Enterprises in 2009, 85 percent of state legislators and 63 percent of local officials say they read and rely on Heartland publications.

Heartland publishes five monthly public policy newspapers – *Budget & Tax News*, *Environment & Climate News*, *Health Care News*, *InfoTech & Telecom News*, and *School Reform News* – featuring the best research and commentary from the nation's free-market think tanks and advocacy groups.

Heartland also manages nine Web sites, including its home site at www.heartland.org and a social media site at www.freedompub.org. It also created and hosts PolicyBot, an online database and search engine for the work of some 350 think tanks and advocacy groups.

Approximately 120 academics and professional economists participate in Heartland's peer review process, and more than 180 elected officials serve on its Legislative Forum. Heartland's full-time staff of government relations professionals interacts daily with hundreds of elected officials across the country, and its public relations and media specialists help shape public opinion by writing and placing dozens of letters to the editor and opinion editorials each week.

Heartland has offices in Chicago, Illinois and Washington, DC, a full-time staff of 35, and a 2010 budget of $7 million. It is supported by the voluntary contributions of approximately 1,800 supporters. For more information, please visit our Web site at www.heartland.org, call 312/377-4000, or write to The Heartland Institute, 19 South LaSalle Street, Suite 903, Chicago, Illinois 60603.